Polished Spiral Karin Kuhlmann

"Although the creation of fractals is bounded to strict mathematical rules, the results are always very inspiring."– Karin Kuhlmann

RADE
4

Moving Between Solids and Silhouettes

3-D Geometry and Measurement

UNIT 7

Investigations

IN NUMBER, DATA, AND SPACE®

Editorial offices: Glenview, Illinois • Parsippany, New Jersey • New York, New York
Sales offices: Boston, Massachusetts • Duluth, Georgia
Glenview, Illinois • Coppell, Texas • Sacramento, California • Mesa, Arizona

The Investigations curriculum was developed by TERC, Cambridge, MA.

This material is based on work supported by the National Science Foundation ("NSF") under Grant No. ESI-0095450. Any opinions, findings, and conclusions or recommendations expressed in this material are those of the author(s) and do not necessarily reflect the views of the National Science Foundation.

ISBN: 0-328-23759-0

ISBN: 978-0-328-23759-3

3 4 5 6 7 8 9 10-V003-15 14 13 12 11 10 09 08 07

CC:N1

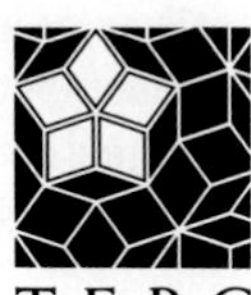

Co-Principal Investigators

Susan Jo Russell

Karen Economopoulos

Authors

Lucy Wittenberg
Director Grades 3–5

Karen Economopoulos
Director Grades K–2

Virginia Bastable
(SummerMath for Teachers, Mt. Holyoke College)

Katie Hickey Bloomfield

Keith Cochran

Darrell Earnest

Arusha Hollister

Nancy Horowitz

Erin Leidl

Megan Murray

Young Oh

Beth W. Perry

Susan Jo Russell

Deborah Schifter
(Education Development Center)

Kathy Sillman

Administrative Staff

Amy Taber
Project Manager

Beth Bergeron

Lorraine Brooks

Emi Fujiwara

Contributing Authors

Denise Baumann

Jennifer DiBrienza

Hollee Freeman

Paula Hooper

Jan Mokros

Stephen Monk
(University of Washington)

Mary Beth O'Connor

Judy Storeygard

Cornelia Tierney

Elizabeth Van Cleef

Carol Wright

Technology

Jim Hammerman

Classroom Field Work

Amy Appell

Rachel E. Davis

Traci Higgins

Julia Thompson

Note: Unless otherwise noted, all contributors listed above were staff of the Education Research Collaborative at TERC during their work on the curriculum. Other affiliations during the time of development are listed.

Collaborating Teachers

This group of dedicated teachers carried out extensive field testing in their classrooms, met regularly to discuss issues of teaching and learning mathematics, provided feedback to staff, welcomed staff into their classrooms to document students' work, and contributed both suggestions and written material that has been incorporated into the curriculum.

Bethany Altchek

Linda Amaral

Kimberly Beauregard

Barbara Bernard

Nancy Buell

Rose Christiansen

Chris Colbath-Hess

Lisette Colon

Kim Cook

Frances Cooper

Kathleen Drew

Rebeka Eston Salemi

Thomas Fisher

Michael Flynn

Holly Ghazey

Susan Gillis

Danielle Harrington

Elaine Herzog

Francine Hiller

Kirsten Lee Howard

Liliana Klass

Leslie Kramer

Melissa Lee Andrichak

Kelley Lee Sadowski

Jennifer Levitan

Mary Lou LoVecchio

Kristen McEnaney

Maura McGrail

Kathe Millett

Florence Molyneaux

Amy Monkiewicz

Elizabeth Monopoli

Carol Murray

Robyn Musser

Christine Norrman

Deborah O'Brien

Timothy O'Connor

Anne Marie O'Reilly

Mark Paige

Margaret Riddle

Karen Schweitzer

Elisabeth Seyferth

Susan Smith

Debra Sorvillo

Shoshanah Starr

Janice Szymaszek

Karen Tobin

JoAnn Trauschke

Ana Vaisenstein

Yvonne Watson

Michelle Woods

Mary Wright

Advisors

Deborah Lowenberg Ball,
University of Michigan

Hyman Bass, Professor of Mathematics and Mathematics Education
University of Michigan

Mary Canner, Principal, Natick Public Schools

Thomas Carpenter, Professor of Curriculum and Instruction,
University of Wisconsin-Madison

Janis Freckmann, Elementary Mathematics Coordinator,
Milwaukee Public Schools

Lynne Godfrey, Mathematics Coach,
Cambridge Public Schools

Ginger Hanlon, Instructional Specialist in Mathematics,
New York City Public Schools

DeAnn Huinker, Director, Center for Mathematics and
Science Education Research, University of Wisconsin-Milwaukee

James Kaput, Professor of Mathematics, University of
Massachusetts-Dartmouth

Kate Kline, Associate Professor, Department of Mathematics
and Statistics, Western Michigan University

Jim Lewis, Professor of Mathematics,
University of Nebraska-Lincoln

William McCallum, Professior of Mathematics,
University of Arizona

Harriet Pollatsek, Professor of Mathematics,
Mount Holyoke College

Debra Shein-Gerson, Elementary Mathematics Specialist,
Weston Public Schools

Gary Shevell, Assistant Principal,
New York City Public Schools

Liz Sweeney, Elementary Math Department,
Boston Public Schools

Lucy West, Consultant, Metamorphosis:
Teaching Learning Communities, Inc.

This revision of the curriculum was built on the work of the many authors who contributed to the first edition (published between 1994 and 1998). We acknowledge the critical contributions of these authors in developing the content and pedagogy of *Investigations*:

Authors

Joan Akers

Michael T. Battista

Douglas H. Clements

Karen Economopoulos

Marlene Kliman

Jan Mokros

Megan Murray

Ricardo Nemirovsky

Andee Rubin

Susan Jo Russell

Cornelia Tierney

Contributing Authors

Mary Berle-Carman

Rebecca B. Corwin

Rebeka Eston

Claryce Evans

Anne Goodrow

Cliff Konold

Chris Mainhart

Sue McMillen

Jerrie Moffet

Tracy Noble

Kim O'Neil

Mark Ogonowski

Julie Sarama

Amy Shulman Weinberg

Margie Singer

Virginia Woolley

Tracey Wright

Contents

UNIT 7

Moving Between Solids and Silhouettes

Investigations

CURRICULUM

Overview of Program Components

FOR TEACHERS

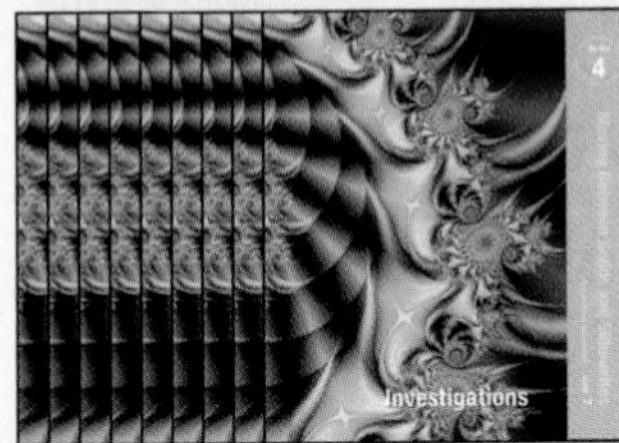

The **Curriculum Units** are the teaching guides. (See far right.)

Implementing Investigations in Grade 4 offers suggestions for implementing the curriculum. It also contains a comprehensive index.

The **Resources Binder** contains all the Resource Masters and Transparencies that support instruction. (Also available on CD) The binder also includes a student software CD.

FOR STUDENTS

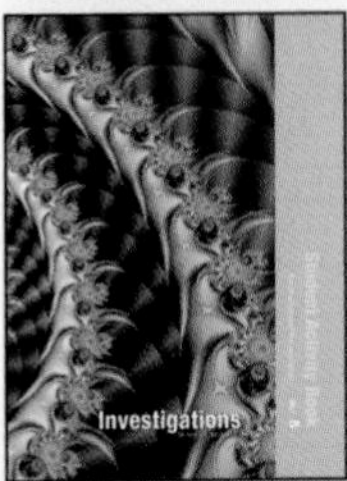

The **Student Activity Book** contains the consumable student pages (Recording Sheets, Homework, Practice, and so on).

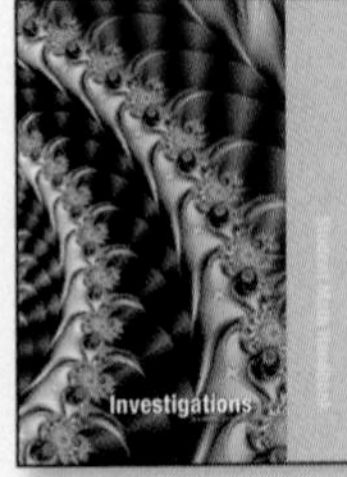

The **Student Math Handbook** contains Math Words and Ideas pages and Games directions.

The *Investigations* Curriculum

Investigations in Number, Data, and Space® is a K–5 mathematics curriculum designed to engage students in making sense of mathematical ideas. Six major goals guided the development of the *Investigations in Number, Data, and Space®* curriculum. The curriculum is designed to:

- Support students to make sense of mathematics and learn that they can be mathematical thinkers
- Focus on computational fluency with whole numbers as a major goal of the elementary grades
- Provide substantive work in important areas of mathematics—rational numbers, geometry, measurement, data, and early algebra—and connections among them
- Emphasize reasoning about mathematical ideas
- Communicate mathematics content and pedagogy to teachers
- Engage the range of learners in understanding mathematics

Underlying these goals are three guiding principles that are touchstones for the *Investigations* team as we approach both students and teachers as agents of their own learning:

1. *Students have mathematical ideas.* Students come to school with ideas about numbers, shapes, measurements, patterns, and data. If given the opportunity to learn in an environment that stresses making sense of mathematics, students build on the ideas they already have and learn about new mathematics they have never encountered. Students learn that they are capable of having mathematical ideas, applying what they know to new situations, and thinking and reasoning about unfamiliar problems.

2. *Teachers are engaged in ongoing learning* about mathematics content, pedagogy, and student learning. The curriculum provides material for professional development, to be used by teachers individually or in groups, that supports teachers' continued learning as they use the curriculum over several years. The *Investigations* curriculum materials are designed as much to be a dialogue with teachers as to be a core of content for students.

3. *Teachers collaborate with the students and curriculum materials* to create the curriculum as enacted in the classroom. The only way for a good curriculum to be used well is for teachers to be active participants in implementing it. Teachers use the curriculum to maintain a clear, focused, and coherent agenda for mathematics teaching. At the same time, they observe and listen carefully to students, try to understand how they are thinking, and make teaching decisions based on these observations.

Investigations is based on experience from research and practice, including field testing that involved documentation of thousands of hours in classrooms, observations of students, input from teachers, and analysis of student work. As a result, the curriculum addresses the learning needs of real students in a wide range of classrooms and communities. The investigations are carefully designed to invite all students into mathematics—girls and boys; members of diverse cultural, ethnic, and language groups; and students with a wide variety of strengths, needs, and interests.

Based on this extensive classroom testing, the curriculum takes seriously the time students need to develop a strong conceptual foundation and skills based on that foundation. Each curriculum unit focuses on an area of content in depth, providing time for students to develop and practice ideas across a variety of activities and contexts that build on each other. Daily guidelines for time spent on class sessions, Classroom Routines (K–3), and Ten-Minute Math (3–5) reflect the commitment to devoting adequate time to mathematics in each school day.

About This Curriculum Unit

This **Curriculum Unit** is one of nine teaching guides in Grade 4. The seventh unit in Grade 4 is *Moving Between Solids and Silhouettes.*

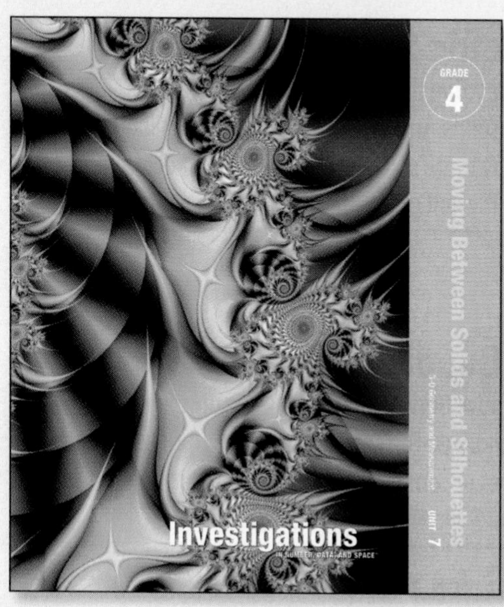

- The **Introduction and Overview** section organizes and presents the instructional materials, provides background information, and highlights important features specific to this unit.
- Each Curriculum Unit contains several **Investigations.** Each Investigation focuses on a set of related mathematical ideas.
- Investigations are divided into one-hour **Sessions,** or lessons.
- Sessions have a combination of these parts: **Activity, Discussion, Math Workshop, Assessment Activity,** and **Session Follow-Up.**
- Each session also has one or more **Ten-Minute Math** activities that are done outside of math time.
- At the back of the book is a collection of **Teacher Notes** and **Dialogue Boxes** that provide professional development related to the unit.
- Also included at the back of the book are the **Student Math Handbook** pages for this unit.
- The **Index** provides a way to look up important words or terms.

Overview

OF THIS UNIT

Investigation	Session	Day	
INVESTIGATION 1 **Geometric Solids** Students describe the properties and attributes of geometric solids. They identify the shapes of silhouettes projected by these solids and visualize what objects look like from different perspectives.	**1.1** What's the Shape?	1	
	1.2 Silhouettes of Geometric Solids	2	
	1.3 City Landscapes	3	
	1.4 Assessment: Match the Silhouettes	4	
INVESTIGATION 2 **Making and Visualizing Cube Buildings** Students move between 2-D and 3-D representations of cube buildings. They draw silhouettes from given perspectives or construct the "building" from given silhouettes.	**2.1** Building with Cubes	5	
	2.2 Drawing Silhouettes of Cube Buildings	6	
	2.3 Drawing Before Building	7	
	2.4 Integrating Views to Make a Cube Building	8	
	2.5 Assessment: Drawing Silhouettes	9	
INVESTIGATION 3 **Understanding Volume** Students find the volume of rectangular prisms in cubic units by constructing boxes to hold arrays of cubes and drawing patterns for those boxes.	**3.1** How Many Cubes?	10	
	3.2 Patterns from the Bottom Up	11	
	3.3 Volume of Boxes	12	
	3.4 Volume of Boxes, *continued*	13	
	3.5 End-of-Unit Assessment	14	

Each *Investigations* session has some combination of these five parts: **Activity, Discussion, Math Workshop, Assessment Activity,** and **Session Follow-Up.** These session parts are indicated in the chart below. Each session also has one or more **Ten-Minute Math** activities that are done outside of math time.

					Ten-Minute Math	
Activity	Discussion	Math Workshop	Assessment Activity	Session Follow-Up	*Quick Images*	*Practicing Place Value*
●●	●			●		●
●●	●			●		●
●●●	●			●		●
●			●	●	●	
●●	●			●	●	
●●	●			●		●
●●	●			●		●
●●	●			●	●	
●	●		●	●	●	
●●	●			●		●
●	●			●		●
	●	●		●	●	
	●	●		●	●	
			●	●	●	

Mathematics

IN THIS UNIT

Moving Between Solids and Silhouettes is the second Grade 4 unit in the Geometry and Measurement strand of *Investigations.* These units develop students' ideas about the attributes of 2-dimensional (2-D) and 3-dimensional (3-D) shapes as students come to understand how these attributes determine a shape's classification. Students also study linear measurement which includes perimeter, area, angles, and volume.

In third grade, students had experiences with examining and building models of polyhedra (the geometric solids used in this unit). They should be familiar with, but not necessarily using, the mathematical vocabulary used to describe prisms and pyramids (face, edge, vertex). Students also have had experience with making open boxes and investigating the number of cubes that fit inside the boxes. They are beginning to understand the idea of volume as they examine the structure of rectangular prisms.

This unit focuses on 3 Mathematical Emphases:

1 Features of Shape **Describing properties of 3-dimensional shapes**

Math Focus Points

- Describing attributes of geometric solids
- Naming geometric solids

Students describe and name geometric solids to become familiar with the components of the shapes. They notice and describe important properties of shape—for example, faces, edges, and vertices. Students begin by using their own language to describe shapes and their components and go on to use mathematical language. In Investigation 1, students select geometric shapes from an envelope and describe the shapes without looking at them. In the rest of the Investigation, students focus on the properties and shapes of the solids.

Students describe and classify geometric solids.

2 Features of Shape **Translating between 2-dimensional and 3-dimensional shapes**

Math Focus Points

- Understanding how 3-D solids project silhouettes with 2-D shapes (for example, how a cone can produce both triangular and circular silhouettes)
- Decomposing images of 3-D shapes and then recombining them to make a given structure
- Visualizing what 3-D figures look like from different perspectives
- Recognizing how components of 3-D cube buildings come together to form the whole building
- Drawing silhouettes of 3-D cube buildings from different perspectives
- Integrating different silhouettes of an object, both to form a mental model and to build the whole object

An important idea in spatial thinking is that objects look different from different points of view. Students not only must recognize the differences, but also must learn to visualize objects from different points of view. In the rest of Investigation 1, students use the geometric solids to explore the silhouettes that different solids can project. They learn, for example, that a cylinder can project both a circular and a rectangular silhouette. They also figure out what views of silhouettes are possible at different points in a given landscape (a specific arrangement of the geometric solids).

Visualizing a 3-dimensional object by looking at a 2-dimensional drawing is a critical spatial skill, as is the reverse, looking at a 3-dimensional object to make a 2-dimensional drawing. These tasks are difficult because a 2-dimensional drawing gives us only partial information about the object that it represents. For example, the diagram below shows only 3 sides of the object. Because the picture is 2-dimensional, it cannot capture all of the information contained in the 3-dimensional object it represents.

The next diagram, showing 3 views of the same object, presents even less information.

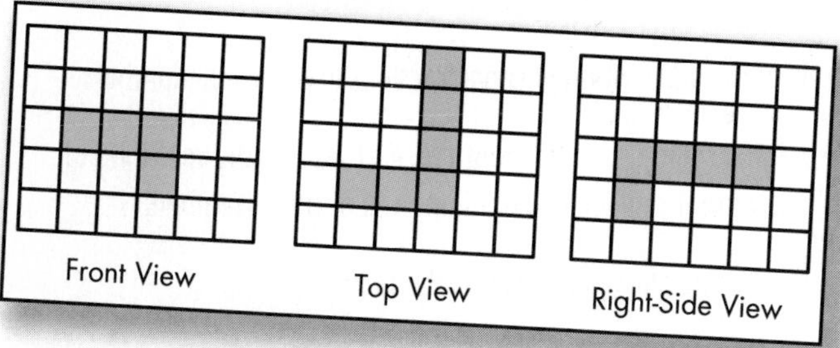

In this drawing, not only do students see only 3 sides, but they also have no information about how the sides are related or should be put together. To interpret either kind of diagram, students must use the partial information given to form a mental model of the entire object.

In Investigation 2, students work between 2-D and 3-D representations. They draw the silhouettes of cube buildings and build the cube buildings from given silhouettes. It is often easier for students to complete these activities than for adults. This is because most adults have not had much experience with this kind of geometric visualization. For many of these activities it is important that you try them yourself before doing them with students. Realize that it is possible that students will complete the tasks more easily than you will.

It is often easier for students to build from silhouettes than for adults.

3 Volume Structuring rectangular prisms and determining their volume

Math Focus Points

- Seeing that cubes filling a rectangular prism can be decomposed into congruent layers
- Finding the volume of cube buildings
- Designing patterns for boxes that hold a given number of cubes (volume)
- Developing a strategy for determining the volume of rectangular prisms
- Finding the number of cubes (volume) that will fit into the box made by a given pattern
- Doubling the number of cubes for a given box and considering how that changes the dimensions of the original box

Volume is an essential concept for students learning 3-dimensional geometry. The volume of a solid is the amount of space that an object occupies, and it is generally measured in cubic units. To understand the measurement of volume, students must develop strategies for determining the number of cubes in 3-D arrays by mentally organizing the cubes—for example, as a stack of 3 rectangular layers, each layer made up of 3 by 4 cubes.

In Investigation 3, students make open rectangular boxes and find ways to determine how many cubes fit inside. Students learn the structure of the rectangular boxes they are trying to measure, as well as the structure of the cube arrays that fit inside. As they work through the Investigation, most students come to determine volume by thinking about the number of cubes in rectangular layers: "A layer contains 3 × 4 cubes—12 cubes—and there are 3 layers, so there are 36 cubes all together." Traditionally, students have been

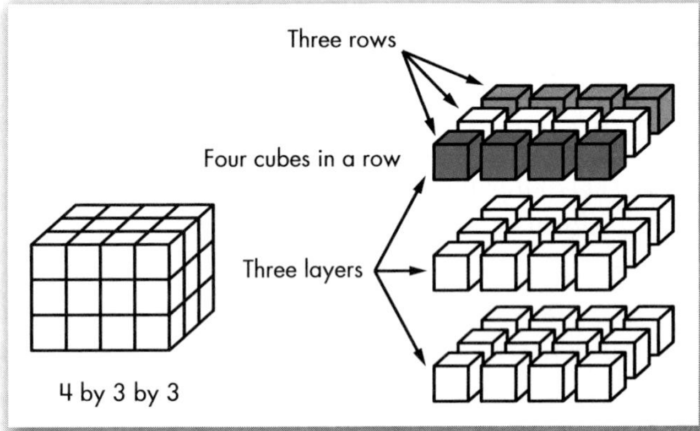

taught to solve such problems with the formula "volume = length × width × height." To use this formula in a meaningful way, students first need to understand the structure of 3-D arrays of cubes. The layering strategies that students invent model volume in a powerful way. This provides an excellent foundation for later work with understanding and applying formulas for volume.

Ten-Minute Math activities focus on

- Reading and writing decimal fractions and decimal numbers
- Adding multiples of one tenth to, and subtracting multiples of one tenth from decimal fractions and decimal numbers
- Organizing and analyzing visual images
- Developing language and concepts needed to communicate about spatial relationships
- Decomposing images of 3-D shapes and then recombining them to make a given structure

In Grade 5, students continue developing their understanding of volume. They determine a general method for finding the volume of any rectangular prism, and they explore the volume of other solid shapes, such as pyramids, cylinders, and cones.

Technology Note

Using the *LogoPaths* Software If you are using the *LogoPaths* software this year, give students ongoing access to the computers **outside of math time** during this unit. *LogoPaths* Resource Masters (M1–M6) offer continued work with *Missing Measures* and *Steps* activities. Students can also continue to play *Mazes* and spend time working with the *Free Explore* option of the software. See **Part 5: Technology in *Investigations:* Calculators and Computers** in *Implementing Investigations in Grade 4:* Introducing and Managing the *LogoPaths* software in Grade 4.

Assessment

IN THIS UNIT

ONGOING ASSESSMENT: Observing Students at Work

The following sessions provide **Ongoing Assessment: Observing Students at Work** opportunities:

- **Session 1.1, p. 25**
- **Session 1.2, p. 30**
- **Session 1.3, p. 38**
- **Session 1.4, p. 42**
- **Session 2.1, pp. 50 and 53**
- **Session 2.2, p. 58**
- **Session 2.3, p. 61**
- **Session 2.4, p. 67**
- **Session 2.5, pp. 70 and 72**
- **Session 3.1, p. 79**
- **Session 3.2, p. 83**
- **Session 3.3, pp. 87 and 88**

WRITING OPPORTUNITIES

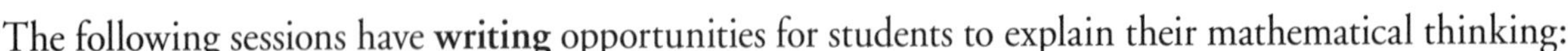

The following sessions have **writing** opportunities for students to explain their mathematical thinking:

- **Session 2.2, pp. 56 and 59**
  Student Activity Book, pp. 21 and 25
- **Session 3.3, p. 89**
  Student Activity Book, p. 48

PORTFOLIO OPPORTUNITIES

The following sessions have work appropriate for a **portfolio:**

- **Session 1.2, p. 29**
  Student Activity Book, p. 5
- **Session 1.4, p. 42**
  M14, Assessment: Match the Silhouettes
- **Session 2.4, p. 65**
  Student Activity Book, p. 30
- **Session 2.5, p. 71**
  M16–M17, Assessment: Drawing Silhouettes
- **Session 3.2, pp. 82–83**
  Student Activity Book, pp. 39–42
- **Session 3.3, p. 86**
  Student Activity Book, p. 45
- **Session 3.5, p. 95**
  M23–M25: End-of-Unit Assessment

Assessing the Benchmarks

Observing students as they engage in conversation about their ideas is a primary means to assess their mathematical understanding. Consider all of your students' work, not just the written assessments. See the chart below for suggestions about key activities to observe.

Checklist Available

Benchmarks in This Unit	Key Activities to Observe	Assessment
1. Identify 2-dimensional silhouettes of 3-dimensional solids (e.g., a cone can project a triangular silhouette).	**Session 1.2:** Matching Solids and Silhouettes	**Session 1.4:** Match the Silhouettes
2. Draw 2-dimensional representations showing different perspectives of a 3-dimensional object.	**Session 2.3:** Silhouettes of Buildings	**Session 2.5:** Drawing Silhouettes **Session 3.5 End-of-Unit Assessment:** Problem 1
3. Find the volume of cube buildings and rectangular prisms.	**Session 3.1:** How Many Cubes? **Session 3.3 and 3.4:** Finding the Volume of More Boxes **Session 3.3 and 3.4:** Double the Number of Cubes	**Session 3.5 End-of-Unit Assessment:** Problems 2 and 3

Relating the Mathematical Emphases to the Benchmarks

Mathematical Emphases	Benchmarks
Features of Shape Translating between 2-dimensional and 3-dimensional shapes	**1 and 2**
Volume Structuring rectangular prisms and determining their volume	**3 and 4**

Ten-Minute Math

IN THIS UNIT

Ten-Minute Math offers practice and review of key concepts for this grade level. These daily activities, to be done in ten minutes outside of math class, are introduced in a unit and repeated throughout the grade. Specific directions for the day's activity are provided in each session. For the full description and variations of each classroom activity, see *Implementing Investigations in Grade 4.*

Activity	Introduced	Full Description of Activity and Its Variations
Practicing Place Value	Unit 5, Session 1.3	*Implementing Investigations in Grade 4*
Quick Images: 3-D	Unit 1, Session 2.1	*Implementing Investigations in Grade 4*

Practicing Place Value

Students practice reading, writing, and saying decimal numbers. They add and subtract multiples of one tenth, and examine how these operations increase or decrease the values of the digits in each place.

Math Focus Points

- Reading and writing decimal fractions and decimal numbers
- Adding multiples of one tenth to, and subtracting multiples of one tenth from, decimal fractions and decimal numbers

Quick Images

Students visualize and analyze images of 3-D geometric figures. After briefly viewing an image of a 3-D structure, students build it from the mental image they formed during the brief viewing.

Math Focus Points

- Organizing and analyzing visual images
- Developing language and concepts needed to communicate about spatial relationships
- Decomposing images of 3-D shapes and then recombining them to make a given structure

Practice and Review

IN THIS UNIT

Practice and review play a critical role in the *Investigations* program. The following components and features are available to provide regular reinforcement of key mathematical concepts and procedures.

Books	Features	In This Unit . . .
Curriculum Unit	**Ten-Minute Math** offers practice and review of key concepts for this grade level. These daily activities, to be done in ten minutes outside of math class, are introduced in a unit and repeated throughout the grade. Specific directions for the day's activity are provided in each session. For the full description and variations of each classroom activity, see *Implementing Investigations in Grade 4.*	• **All sessions**
Student Activity Book	**Daily Practice** pages in the *Student Activity Book* provide one of three types of written practice: **reinforcement** of the content of the unit, **ongoing review,** or **enrichment** opportunities. Some Daily Practice pages will also have Ongoing Review items with multiple-choice problems similar to those on standardized tests.	• **All sessions**
	Homework pages in the *Student Activity Book* are an extension of the work done in class. At times they help students prepare for upcoming activities.	• **Session 1.1** • **Session 1.3** • **Session 1.4** • **Session 2.1** • **Session 2.2** • **Session 2.4** • **Session 3.1** • **Session 3.2** • **Session 3.3**
Student Math Handbook	**Math Words and Ideas** in the *Student Math Handbook* are pages that summarize key words and ideas. Most Words and Ideas pages have at least one exercise.	• **Student Math Handbook, pp. 63, 118–126**
	Games pages are found in a section of the *Student Math Handbook.*	• **No games are introduced in this unit.**

Differentiation

IN THIS UNIT

Supporting the Range of Learners

Sessions	1.1	1.2	1.3	1.4	2.1	2.3	2.4	2.5	3.1	3.2	3.3
Intervention	•		•	•	•	•		•	•	•	•
Extension		•		•		•	•				•
ELL	•				•						•

Intervention

Suggestions are made to support and engage students who are having difficulty with a particular idea, activity, or problem.

Extension

Suggestions are made to support and engage students who finish early or may be ready for additional challenges.

English Language Learners (ELL)

As students work through the material in this unit, they will encounter vocabulary about 3-D shapes and measurement that may be new to them. You can help English Language Learners master this vocabulary by using it in the context of various activities and by providing consistent visual supports. The Math Words and Ideas pages in the *Student Math Handbook* can be a particularly useful reference for the English Language Learners in your classroom. Students can also create their own word banks to include native language translations or additional vocabulary not included in the Math Words and Ideas pages. Students can add to these word banks throughout the unit. Whenever possible, ask students to review the vocabulary independently or in pairs.

Throughout this unit, students discuss their ideas while working with partners and in whole class discussions. Pairing English Language Learners with Native English speakers will help them develop their mathematical vocabulary. You can provide other assistance to help English Language Learners participate more fully in class discussions. For example, you may wish to meet with them before some class discussions to preview the questions you plan to ask. By giving them the chance to formulate and practice answers ahead of time, you can better assess their understanding of the math content and provide them with the language they may require.

Working with the Range of Learners: Classroom Cases is a set of episodes written by teachers that focuses on meeting the needs of the range of learners in the classroom. In the first section, *Setting up the Mathematical Community,* teachers write about how they create a supportive and productive learning environment in their classrooms. In the next section, *Accommodations for Learning,* teachers focus on specific modifications they make to meet the needs of some of their learners. In the last section, *Language and Representation,* teachers share how they help students use representations and develop language to investigate and express mathematical ideas. The questions at the end of each case provide a starting point for your own reflection or for discussion with colleagues. See *Implementing Investigations in Grade 4* for this set of episodes.

INVESTIGATION 1

Mathematical Emphases

Features of Shape Describing properties of 3-dimensional shapes

Math Focus Points

- Describing attributes of geometric solids
- Naming geometric solids

Features of Shape Translating between 2-dimensional and 3-dimensional shapes

Math Focus Points

- Understanding how 3-D solids project silhouettes with 2-D shapes (for example, how a cone can produce both triangular and circular silhouettes)
- Decomposing images of 3-D shapes and then recombining them to make a given structure
- Visualizing what 3-D figures look like from different perspectives

Geometric Solids

Session	Student Activity Book	Student Math Handbook	Professional Development: Read Ahead of Time
SESSION 1.1 p. 22 **What's the Shape?** Students describe the properties and attributes of geometric solids.	1–3	118–121	• **Part 4: Ten Minute Math:** in *Implementing Investigations in Grade 4:* Practicing Place Value • **Mathematics in This Unit,** p. 10
SESSION 1.2 p. 27 **Silhouettes of Geometric Solids** Students identify the shapes of silhouettes projected by geometric solids.	5–6	122–123	• **Teacher Note:** Difficulties in Visualizing Silhouettes, p. 97
SESSION 1.3 p. 33 **City Landscapes** Students build "landscapes" by using geometric solids and visualize what objects look like from different perspectives.	7–9	122–123	• **Part 4: Ten Minute Math:** in *Implementing Investigations in Grade 4:* Quick Images: 3-D • **Dialogue Box:** Seeing Cube Buildings in Our Minds, p. 112
SESSION 1.4 p. 40 **Assessment: Match the Silhouettes** Students continue building "landscapes" and visualizing what objects look like from different perspectives. They are assessed on their ability to match silhouettes with drawings of the 3-D shapes.	11–15	122–123	• **Teacher Note:** Assessment: Match the Silhouettes, p. 99 • **Dialogue Box:** Good Thinking Does Not Always Result in Correct Answers, p. 113

Ten-Minute Math See page 16 for an overview.

Practicing Place Value

- No materials needed

Quick Images

- T74, *Quick Images: 3-D* Cut apart the images and put Images 1–4 aside for this activity (from Session 1.3).
- Connecting cubes (15–20 per student)

Materials to Gather	Materials to Prepare
• **Geometric solids** (1 set per group) • **Large manila envelopes** • **Chart paper**	• **M7–M8, Family Letter** Make copies. (1 per student) • **Geometric solids** Place 4–6 geometric solids in each envelope. (1 set per group) • **Chart paper** Label chart paper "Math Words We Used to Describe the Solids."
• **Blank paper**	• **M9–M10, Family Letter** Make copies. (1 per student) • **Geometric solids** Use small adhesive labels to number the solids from 1–12, numbering all sets of solids the same way (e.g., the cube in each set is number 1, the square prism is number 2, the octagonal prism is number 3, and so on) (1 set per group).
• **Connecting cubes** (20 per student) • **Geometric solids** (1 set per group) • **Toy figures** (1 per set of solids) • **Chart paper** (1 sheet per group)	• **T74, *Quick Images: 3-D*** Cut apart.
• **Geometric solids** (1 set per group) • **Toy figures** (1 per set of solids)	• **M14, Assessment: Match the Silhouettes** Make copies. (1 per student)

Overhead Transparency

SESSION 1.1

What's the Shape?

Math Focus Points

- Describing attributes of geometric solids
- Naming geometric solids

Vocabulary

prism
cylinder
solid
vertex
edge
face

Today's Plan		Materials
1 ACTIVITY **Introducing *What's the Shape?***	20 MIN GROUPS	• *Student Activity Book,* p. 1 • Geometric solids; large manila envelopes*
2 DISCUSSION **Words We Use**	15 MIN CLASS	• Chart: "Math Words We Used to Describe the Solids"*
3 ACTIVITY ***What's the Shape?***	25 MIN GROUPS	• *Student Activity Book,* p. 1 • Geometric solids* (from Activity 1)
4 SESSION FOLLOW-UP **Daily Practice and Homework**		• *Student Activity Book,* pp. 2–3 • *Student Math Handbook,* pp. 118–121 • M7–M8, Family Letter*

*See *Materials to Prepare,* p. 21.

Ten-Minute Math

Practicing Place Value **Write 780.7 on the board and have students practice saying it. Let students know that this number is commonly read both as "seven hundred eighty and seven tenths" and as "seven hundred eighty point seven." Make sure all students can read, write, and say this number correctly. Ask students to solve these problems mentally, if possible:**

- What is 20 more than 780.7?
- What is 100 more?
- What is 100 less?

Write each answer on the board. Ask students to compare each sum and difference with 780.7. Which places have the same digits? Which do not? Why? If time remains, pose additional similar problems using these numbers: 336.5 and 1,514.7.

ACTIVITY

20 MIN GROUPS

Introducing *What's the Shape?*

Organize students in groups of four and introduce the session.

For the next three weeks, we're going to spend some time on geometry. In the last geometry unit, you worked with 2-dimensional shapes, such as rectangles and triangles, and found the perimeter and area of some of these shapes. In this unit, you're going to work with 3-dimensional shapes, such as prisms and cylinders. You will also find the volume of rectangular prisms. First, you're going to do an activity to help you remember the names of 3-D shapes and their attributes.

Give each group one of the envelopes that you prepared. Explain that one student reaches into the envelope, feels an object, and describes it to the group. One student writes the words and phrases used to describe the solid, and the other two students guess what the object is.

Students might say:

"It has square sides."

"All the sides are the same."

After students have described the object as completely as possible and made preliminary guesses, students use *Student Activity Book* page 1 to guess which of the solids is being described. The student removes the object from the envelope, and the group members check to see whether their guesses were correct. Students take turns playing each role.

After each group has played a couple of rounds, call the class together for a whole-class discussion.

DIFFERENTIATION: Supporting the Range of Learners

ELL To help English Language Learners participate more successfully in this activity, you may want to preview the expressions used to describe the attributes of shapes. You can have students make an illustrated vocabulary list to help them access language more quickly

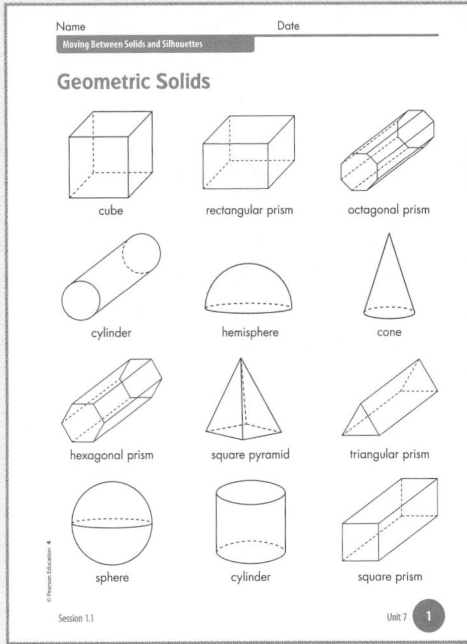
Name Date

Moving Between Solids and Silhouettes

Geometric Solids

Session 1.1 Unit 7 1

▲ Student Activity Book, p. 1

during the activity. You might also give English Language Learners extra time beforehand to create descriptions of the shapes to present to their group members for guessing.

DISCUSSION

Words We Use

15 MIN CLASS

Math Focus Points for Discussion

- Describing attributes of geometric solids

Post the chart titled "Math Words We Used to Describe the Solids." Ask students to share the mathematical words their group used to describe the shapes. As students suggest both informal and formal mathematical language, write the words on the chart, and connect the terms when possible.①

Someone suggested corner and someone else suggested vertex. We're using both of these words to mean the same thing, right? The correct mathematical term for this attribute is vertex.

Other examples include:

- line → edge
- side → face

Although informal language can be useful in describing shapes, precision in language is needed to define and classify shapes. In this discussion, students begin to distinguish between informal and mathematical language. Circle the words vertex, edge, and face on the chart (or add them to the chart if not suggested by students), and indicate to students that these are some of the mathematical terms used in this unit. By the end of the discussion, the chart should look like the following:

side	round	square
(edge)	point	corner
circular	(face)	flat
triangle	long	(vertex)
line	octagon	

Teaching Note

① **Using Mathematical Vocabulary** During the rest of this Investigation, continue using the mathematical vocabulary introduced in Session 1.1. Use the correct names of the solids and refer to their attributes *(rectangular prism, square pyramid, face, vertex, edge,* and so on). It is expected that through continued modeling of mathematical language by the teacher and other students, most students will use the correct mathematical terms.

3 ACTIVITY
What's the Shape?

Students continue playing *What's the Shape?*

Consider having the two guessers also attempt to draw the solid as it is being described. The recorder should continue writing words used. Have brief discussions as necessary to add words to the students' lists of words.

Students use mathematical language to describe geometric solids.

ONGOING ASSESSMENT: Observing Students at Work

Students describe attributes and properties of geometric solids.

- **How are students describing the solids?** Are they comparing the shape to another object ("like a ball"), or are they describing attributes (number of faces, vertices, and so on)?

DIFFERENTIATION: Supporting the Range of Learners

Intervention Some students may have difficulty moving beyond description of the entire shape to description of its component parts. Some possibilities for helping these students include joining the game for a couple of turns in order to model describing the shapes. Ask questions about the number of faces, edges, and vertices and about the shape of the faces, in order to encourage students to attend to these attributes.

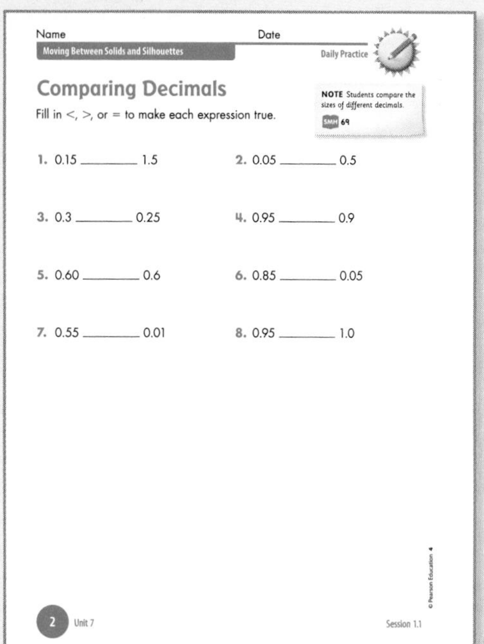
Name Date

Moving Between Solids and Silhouettes — Daily Practice

Comparing Decimals

Fill in <, >, or = to make each expression true.

NOTE Students compare the sizes of different decimals.

SMH 69

1. 0.15 ______ 1.5
2. 0.05 ______ 0.5
3. 0.3 ______ 0.25
4. 0.95 ______ 0.9
5. 0.60 ______ 0.6
6. 0.85 ______ 0.05
7. 0.55 ______ 0.01
8. 0.95 ______ 1.0

2 Unit 7 — Session 1.1

▲ Student Activity Book, p. 2

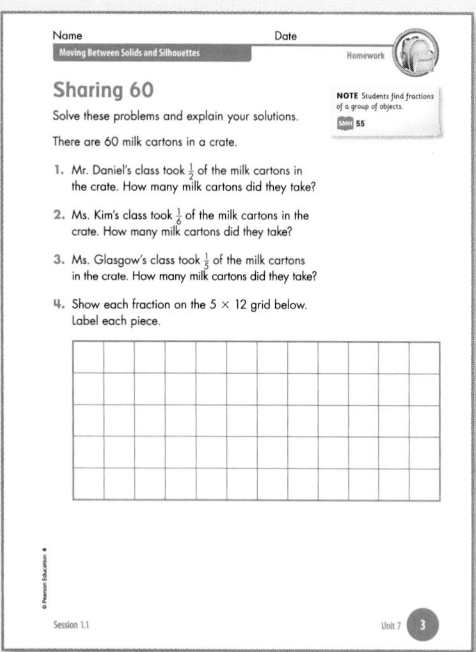
Name Date

Moving Between Solids and Silhouettes — Homework

Sharing 60

Solve these problems and explain your solutions.

NOTE Students find fractions of a group of objects.

SMH 55

There are 60 milk cartons in a crate.

1. Mr. Daniel's class took $\frac{1}{2}$ of the milk cartons in the crate. How many milk cartons did they take?
2. Ms. Kim's class took $\frac{1}{6}$ of the milk cartons in the crate. How many milk cartons did they take?
3. Ms. Glasgow's class took $\frac{1}{5}$ of the milk cartons in the crate. How many milk cartons did they take?
4. Show each fraction on the 5 × 12 grid below. Label each piece.

Session 1.1 — Unit 7 3

▲ Student Activity Book, p. 3

4 SESSION FOLLOW-UP

Daily Practice and Homework

Daily Practice: For ongoing review, have students complete *Student Activity Book* page 2.

Homework: Ask students to complete *Student Activity Book* page 3, on which they find fractions of a group of objects.

Student Math Handbook: Students and families may use *Student Math Handbook* pages 118–121 for reference and review. See pages 119–121 in the back of this unit.

Family Letter: Send home copies of the Family Letter (M7–M8).

Silhouettes of Geometric Solids

Math Focus Points

- Understanding how 3-D solids project silhouettes with 2-D shapes (for example, how a cone can produce both triangular and circular silhouettes)

Vocabulary

silhouette

Today's Plan			Materials
1 ACTIVITY **Introducing Matching Solids and Silhouettes**	15 MIN	CLASS	• Geometric solids (from Session 1.1) • Blank paper
2 ACTIVITY **Matching Solids and Silhouettes**	25 MIN	PAIRS	• *Student Activity Book*, p. 5 • Geometric solids*
3 DISCUSSION **Checking Silhouettes**	20 MIN	CLASS	• *Student Activity Book*, p. 5 • Geometric solids*
4 SESSION FOLLOW-UP **Daily Practice**			• *Student Activity Book*, p. 6 • *Student Math Handbook*, pp. 122–123 • M9–M10, Family Letter*

*See *Materials to Prepare*, p. 21.

Ten-Minute Math

Practicing Place Value Say "two hundred two and eight tenths," and ask students to write the number. Make sure that all students can read, write, and say this number correctly. Ask students to solve these problems mentally, if possible:

- What is 202.8 + 200?
- 202.8 + 300?
- 202.8 + 400?
- 202.8 − 200?

Write each answer on the board. Ask students to compare each sum and difference with 202.8. Which places have the same digits? Which do not? Why? If time remains, pose additional similar problems using these numbers: 302.36 and 680.9.

Teaching Note

① **Using The Term *Silhouette*** For the purposes of this Investigation, a silhouette is the flat, dark shape produced when an object blocks light. Only the outline of the object is seen; it is like a shadow.

ACTIVITY

Introducing Matching Solids and Silhouettes

Ask whether any student can tell the class something about silhouettes① and how they are produced.

Illustrate the concept of silhouette by placing your hand on the overhead projector. Explain that the mirror above your hand reflects the light from the glass so that the silhouette projects onto the wall or a screen instead of onto the ceiling.

Have available the set of 12 geometric solids that students used in Session 1.1. Briefly review the names of the shape. Use the correct names and encourage students to do so as well.

Shut off the projector's light and hold up the large cube from the geometric solids set, keeping one face toward the students.

What do you think the cube's **silhouette** will look like when I put it on the overhead, like this?

(Place the cube on the glass so that it is directly underneath the mirror, with the face that you showed the class facing down.)

Draw what you think the silhouette will look like.

When students have finished drawing, turn on the overhead light. (You should practice making the silhouettes with the solids before class so that you are familiar with the results.)

Does your drawing look like the actual silhouette? If not, how is it different?

Repeat this procedure with the narrow cylinder. Show students the circular base of the cylinder, and then place the base on the glass of the overhead projector with the light off. Ask students to draw the silhouettes. Walk around the classroom to see what they draw. When most students have finished drawing, turn on the projector's light again so that students can discuss the actual shape.

Ask students whether their drawings of the silhouette were correct.

Next, ask students to draw the silhouette shape of the cylinder's curved side. Hold up the cylinder with its top and bottom horizontal, showing the long, curved side. Then lay the cylinder on its side on the overhead projector glass with the light off.

As students draw, walk around the classroom to see their ideas. After everyone has finished, turn on the overhead. This problem may be a bit more difficult because students may not have had much experience with this type of visualization.

Many people (students and adults) do not expect a curved figure to produce a rectangular silhouette.

Can you find something else in the room that has a rectangular silhouette?

Test students' ideas by putting the objects that they suggest on the overhead projector, if possible.

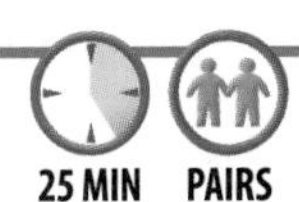

ACTIVITY

2 Matching Solids and Silhouettes

Direct students' attention to *Student Activity Book* page 5. Tell students that they will work in pairs on this activity, so each group of 4 from Session 1.1 will need to figure out how to share their set of solids. Draw students' attention to the numbers with which you have labeled each solid.

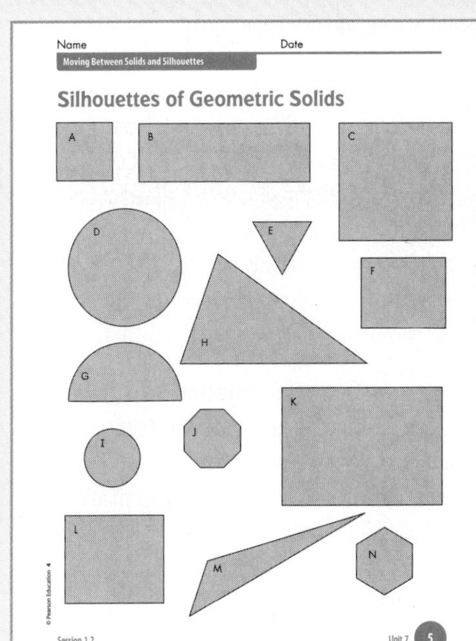

Name Date

Moving Between Solids and Silhouettes

Silhouettes of Geometric Solids

A B C D E F G H I J K L M N

© Pearson Education 4

Session 1.2 Unit 7 5

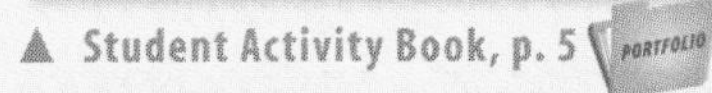

▲ Student Activity Book, p. 5 PORTFOLIO

Teaching Notes

❷ **Checking for Discrepancies** Because of manufacturing variations, the solids and the silhouettes may vary slightly in size. Compare your solids with the silhouettes ahead of time to see whether there are any size discrepancies. If there are, make allowances for "mistakes" that may be due to these discrepancies rather than to conceptual problems.

❹ **Using the Overhead Projector** The overhead projector is an essential tool for helping students understand silhouettes. It provides silhouettes that students can actually see rather than merely imagine; it gives them something concrete that they can manipulate. Repeatedly urge students to "prove" their answers by using the overhead projector.

Professional Development

❸ **Teacher Note:** Difficulties in Visualizing Silhouettes, p. 97

Look at each silhouette on the sheet and try to find all of the geometric solids that could make that shape. Beside or below each silhouette, write the number of every solid you think could make that silhouette.

Tell students that the silhouettes on the sheet are nearly the same size as the solids and that size is important in making their matches.❷ A silhouette might have the same shape as a solid, but the sizes might be different. (For example, see Silhouettes D and I.) A silhouette might not have a matching solid. "None" is a possible answer.❸

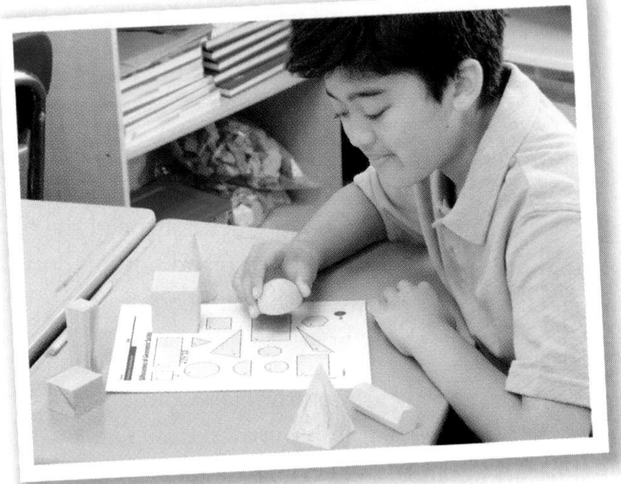

Students may place the solids directly on the Student Activity Book *page to find the correct silhouettes.*

Encourage students to use the overhead projector to see the actual silhouettes. Remind students that a silhouette is a projection of the surface or face of a solid that is facing down.❹

ONGOING ASSESSMENT: Observing Students at Work

Students match solids to silhouettes.

- **How do students match the solids and silhouettes?** Do they put the solids right on the paper? Do they use the overhead projector?
- **Do students recognize that the curved solids have the potential to cast rectangular silhouettes?**

DIFFERENTIATION: Supporting the Range of Learners

Extension Students who finish early can select everyday objects in the classroom, draw their silhouettes, and then use the overhead to see the silhouettes.

3 DISCUSSION

Checking Silhouettes

Math Focus Points for Discussion

- Understanding how 3-D solids project silhouettes with 2-D shapes (for example, how a cone can produce both triangular and circular silhouettes)

Have a discussion with students about the silhouettes on *Student Activity Book* page 5. Discuss silhouettes that:

- could be made by multiple shapes;
- cause students difficulty;
- cause disagreement among students over which solids they match.

Solids with curves seem to cause the most confusion. Encourage students to use the mathematical names for these solids. Have students bring the solids to the projector to defend their answers.

The following list shows reasonable answers for this activity. However, any answer that students can justify or prove is acceptable.

Name Date

Moving Between Solids and Silhouettes

Daily Practice

Don't Block My Shadow

Circle all the silhouettes that can be made with each solid.

NOTE Students determine which silhouettes can be made from a given solid.

SMH 122–123

1.

2.

3.

Ongoing Review

4. Which shape has only flat surfaces?

A. B. C. D.

6 Unit 7 Session 1.2

▲ Student Activity Book, p. 6

Silhouette	Solids That Can Make the Silhouette
A	square prism
B	square prism, triangular prism, narrow cylinder, octagonal prism, hexagonal prism (may be too large)
C	large cube, wide cylinder
D	sphere, hemisphere, wide cylinder
E	triangular prism
F	rectangular prism
G	hemisphere
H	square pyramid, cone
I	narrow cylinder
J	octagonal prism
K	large cube (viewed looking straight on at one edge)
L	rectangular prism
M	none
N	hexagonal prism

4

SESSION FOLLOW-UP

Daily Practice

Daily Practice: For reinforcement of this unit's content, have students complete *Student Activity Book* page 6.

Student Math Handbook: Students and families may use *Student Math Handbook* pages 122–123 for reference and review. See pages 119–121 in the back of this unit.

Family Letter: Send home copies of the Family Letter (M9–M10).

City Landscapes

Math Focus Points

- Decomposing images of 3-D shapes and then recombining them to make a given structure
- Visualizing what 3-D figures look like from different perspectives
- Understanding how 3-D solids project silhouettes with 2-D shapes (for example, how a cone can produce both triangular and circular silhouettes)

Today's Plan			Materials
1 ACTIVITY **Introducing *Quick Images***	10 MIN	CLASS	• T74* • Connecting cubes
2 ACTIVITY **Introducing City Landscapes**	20 MIN	GROUPS, CLASS	• *Student Activity Book,* p. 7 • Geometric solids; chart paper; toy figures
3 ACTIVITY **What Can You See from Here?**	15 MIN	GROUPS	• *Student Activity Book,* p. 7 • Geometric solids; chart paper; toy figures
4 DISCUSSION **City Landscapes**	15 MIN	CLASS	• *Student Activity Book,* p. 7 • Geometric solids
5 SESSION FOLLOW-UP **Daily Practice and Homework**			• *Student Activity Book,* pp. 8–9 • *Student Math Handbook,* pp. 122–123

*See *Materials to Prepare,* p. 21.

Ten-Minute Math

Practicing Place Value Write 41.4 on the board and have students practice saying it. Let students know that this number is commonly read as both "forty-one and four tenths" and "forty-one point four." Make sure all students can read, write, and say this number correctly.

Ask students to solve these problems mentally, if possible:

- What is one tenth more than 41.4?
- What is five tenths more?
- What is 10 more?

Write each answer on the board. Ask students to compare each sum with 41.4. Which places have the same digits? Which do not? Why? If time remains, pose additional similar problems using these numbers: 59.5 and 64.19.

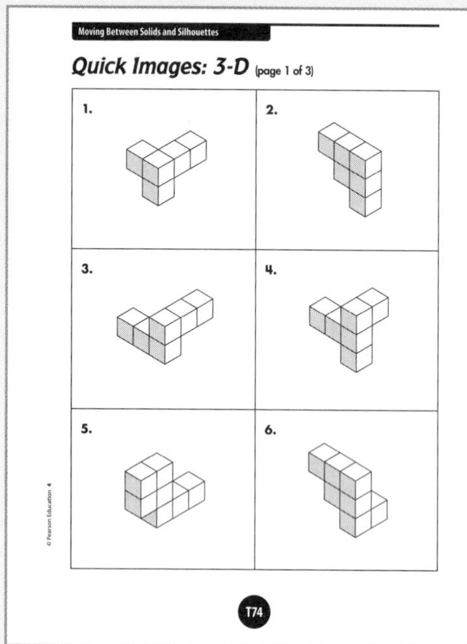

Moving Between Solids and Silhouettes

Quick Images: 3-D (page 1 of 3)

1. 2.

3. 4.

5. 6.

© Pearson Education 4

T74

▲ Transparencies, T74

ACTIVITY 1

Introducing *Quick Images*

Quick Images: 3-D, a Ten-Minute Math activity, is used in each investigation of this unit. Give each student a supply of 20 connecting cubes. All students should be seated facing the overhead screen. Explain the activity.

Do you remember how we've done *Quick Images* at other times during this year? This time, we're going to use 3-D shapes called cube buildings. I will flash a picture of a cube building on the overhead for 3 seconds. Look at it carefully. When I turn off the overhead, try to see the cube building in your mind. Then use your cubes to make the building that you saw. I will flash the picture again after everyone has had time to try building it.

Flash the transparency of Image 1 from *Quick Images: 3-D* (T74) on the overhead for 3 seconds. It is important to keep the picture up for as close to 3 seconds as possible. If you show the picture for too long, students may build from the picture rather than from their mental image of it. If you show it for too brief a time, they will not have time to form a mental image.

Give students time to work with their cubes. After you see that most students have stopped building, call students' attention to the overhead and flash the picture again for another 3 seconds. It is essential to provide enough time between the first and second flashes for most students to have completed their buildings. They should have done all that they could, before seeing the picture on the screen again.

Students decompose the mental image they form and then recompose it with the connecting cubes.

When the building activity subsides again, show the picture a third time. This time, leave it visible so that all students can complete or revise their solutions.

After students are satisfied that their buildings are complete, ask questions such as these:

- How did you see the cube building in your mind?
- Did you break it into different parts? If so, how?
- How were you able to remember the entire structure?[1]

Continue the same activity, using Image 2.

2 ACTIVITY

20 MIN GROUPS CLASS

Introducing City Landscapes

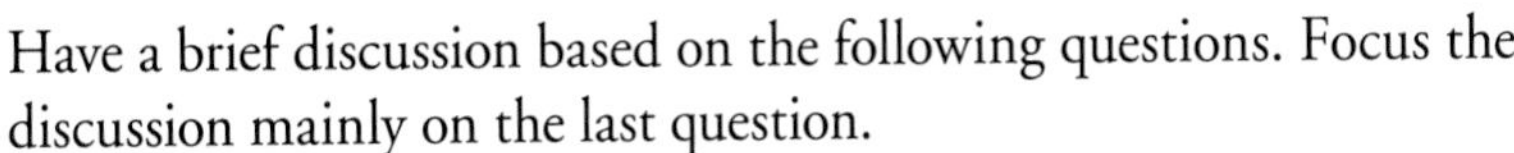

Have a brief discussion based on the following questions. Focus the discussion mainly on the last question.

Who can show us a solid that makes silhouettes with different shapes? What shapes will it make? Are there other solids that make several silhouette shapes? How can one solid make different silhouette shapes?

Students should understand that as they look at a solid from different positions, they might see different silhouettes. For example, looking at a cylinder from the end, they see a circular silhouette; from the side, a rectangular shape.

Organize your class in groups of 4. Give each group a set of solids and a blank sheet of paper. Direct students' attention to Landscape 1 at the top of *Student Activity Book* page 7.

This diagram shows a particular landscape, or arrangement, of 9 geometric solids. Each group is going to build this arrangement. Place your solids on the plain white paper exactly as shown in the diagram. When you have finished, everyone in the group should agree that your landscape matches the diagram.

Circulate around the room and observe students. As they discuss the solids, encourage students to use the shapes' mathematical names. It is important to have all of the students set up their solids on standard-size paper because their answers may differ if the distance between solids varies.

Professional Development

[1] **Dialogue Box:** Seeing Cube Buildings in Our Minds, p. 112

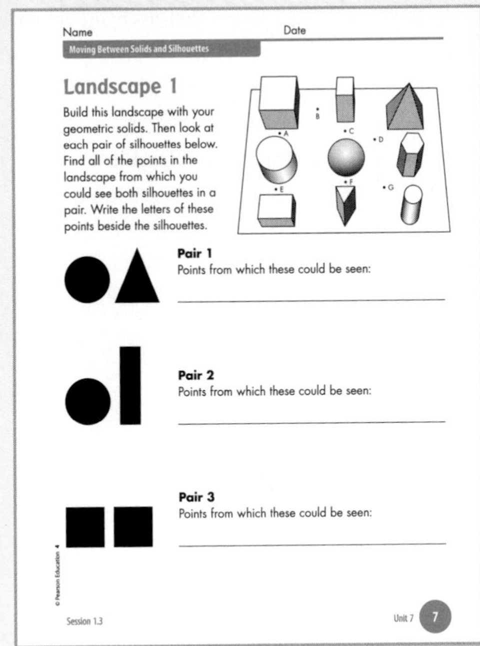

Name Date

Moving Between Solids and Silhouettes

Landscape 1

Build this landscape with your geometric solids. Then look at each pair of silhouettes below. Find all of the points in the landscape from which you could see both silhouettes in a pair. Write the letters of these points beside the silhouettes.

Pair 1
Points from which these could be seen:

Pair 2
Points from which these could be seen:

Pair 3
Points from which these could be seen:

Session 1.3 Unit 7 7

▲ **Student Activity Book, p. 7**

Teaching Note

❷ **Showing the Correct Perspective on the Overhead** In order to show the proper silhouette, you must change the positioning of the figure from vertical to horizontal. If your students question your positioning, explain that the mirror on the projector is like the eyes of the toy figure looking at the square prism. To help students understand the change, it may be helpful to position the toy figure up underneath the mirror with its feet toward the screen so that it looks directly down at the prism. This change of perspective is difficult for students to understand, so do not belabor the point.

When the landscapes are built, have each group of students place a toy figure at point B, referring to the diagram to find that position.

What will the silhouette of the rectangular prism look like to your toy figure? [Hold the prism upright.] Draw what you think it will look like from the toy's position.

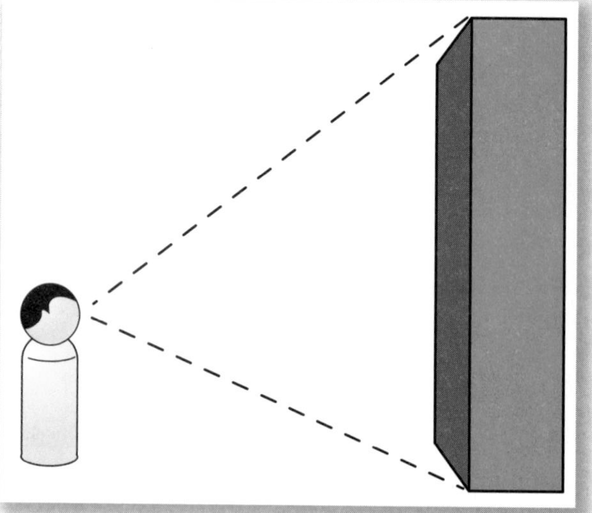

After students have finished drawing, show the silhouette of the rectangular prism by placing it on the overhead glass.❷

Does this silhouette look like what you drew? Why or why not?

Next, direct students' attention back to *Student Activity Book* page 7.

Look at the first pair of silhouettes below the diagram for Landscape 1. On the diagram, find a point with a letter where your toy figure could stand and see both of these silhouettes. You can choose any point, and the toy figure can be facing in any direction.

If you think you know an answer, put your toy figure at that point in your landscape, and try to convince the others in your group that someone could see both silhouettes from that position. You might have to crouch down and get behind your figure to see the solids from the figure's viewpoint. Remember that it's not only the shape of the silhouettes that is important; the size matters, too. If the silhouette shows a large square, you must find a point from which you would see a large square silhouette.

Students look at solids from different positions and see different silhouettes.

Give groups a few minutes to complete this task. When most groups have agreed on a point or points, call the class back together. Ask students to explain and defend their answers.

For Pair 1, some students might say the answer is point D, and others might say point C. Both answers are reasonable. Some students, however, might say point G. Notice that from point G, the figure will not get an unobstructed view of the entire pyramid. Some students will not understand what is wrong with point G unless they position the toy figure at G—facing toward the square pyramid—and crouch behind the toy to see exactly what it is "seeing." This is an example of recognizing that the square pyramid projects a triangular silhouette but does not result in the correct answer for this problem.

ACTIVITY

15 MIN GROUPS

3 What Can You See from Here?

Have students identify the next two pairs of silhouettes on *Student Activity Book* page 7. Students find, test, and justify their answers by moving the toy figure around to different points in the landscape and then getting behind it to "see as it sees."

Students will continue this activity in the next session on *Student Activity Book* pages 11 and 12.

Students should have access to the overhead projector to test their ideas.

ONGOING ASSESSMENT: Observing Students at Work

Students match pairs of silhouettes to geometric solids.

- **How do students decide what solids the silhouettes represent?**
- **Do they crouch down in order to see from the same perspective as the toy figure?**
- **How easily are they able to visualize the silhouettes?**
- **What names are students using for the solids?** Are they using mathematical names or informal names?

DIFFERENTIATION: Supporting the Range of Learners

Intervention Students who are continuing to develop their ideas of perspective and silhouettes may use simpler landscapes, with just three or four solids.

DISCUSSION

City Landscapes

15 MIN CLASS

Math Focus Points for Discussion

- Understanding how 3-D solids project silhouettes with 2-D shapes (for example, how a cone can produce both triangular and circular silhouettes)

As a class, discuss students' solutions to Pair 2 and Pair 3 on *Student Activity Book* page 7. For each problem, students must justify their answers. Encourage students to challenge any answers that they believe are incorrect. Students should discuss disagreements until they reach a consensus. Use the overhead to help students reach agreement regarding a solution.

Reasonable answers for Pairs 1–3 are shown below. Let students decide which answers they will accept as correct; students sometimes make a good case for answers that are not listed. Watch for and encourage good reasoning as students discuss how 2-D silhouettes represent 3-D shapes.

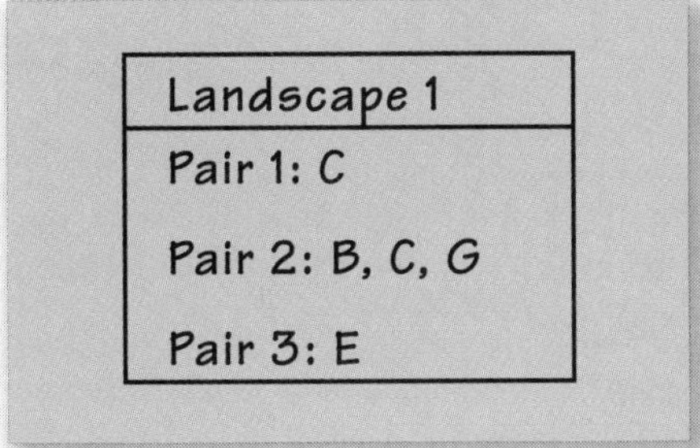

5 SESSION FOLLOW-UP
Daily Practice and Homework

Daily Practice: For ongoing review, have students complete *Student Activity Book* page 8.

Homework: Students find objects at home that match given silhouettes on *Student Activity Book* page 9.

Student Math Handbook: Students and families may use *Student Math Handbook* pages 122–123 for reference and review. See pages 119–121 in the back of this unit.

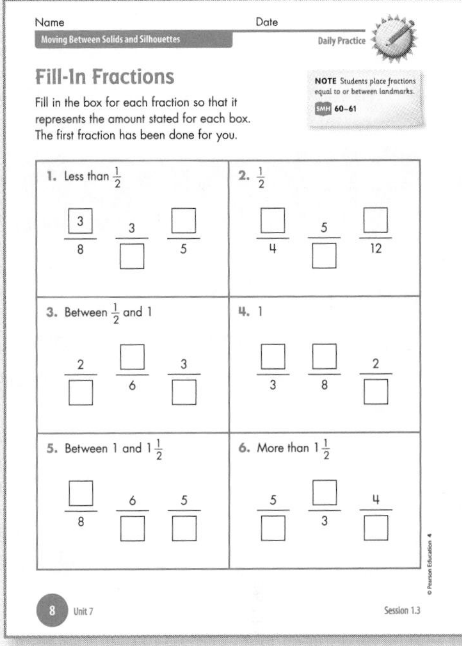

Name Date

Moving Between Solids and Silhouettes — Daily Practice

Fill-In Fractions

NOTE Students place fractions equal to or between landmarks. SMH 60–61

Fill in the box for each fraction so that it represents the amount stated for each box. The first fraction has been done for you.

1. Less than $\frac{1}{2}$: $\frac{3}{8}$, $\frac{3}{\square}$, $\frac{\square}{5}$

2. $\frac{1}{2}$: $\frac{\square}{4}$, $\frac{5}{\square}$, $\frac{\square}{12}$

3. Between $\frac{1}{2}$ and 1: $\frac{2}{\square}$, $\frac{\square}{6}$, $\frac{3}{\square}$

4. 1: $\frac{\square}{3}$, $\frac{\square}{8}$, $\frac{2}{\square}$

5. Between 1 and $1\frac{1}{2}$: $\frac{\square}{8}$, $\frac{6}{\square}$, $\frac{5}{\square}$

6. More than $1\frac{1}{2}$: $\frac{5}{\square}$, $\frac{\square}{3}$, $\frac{4}{\square}$

© Pearson Education 4

8 Unit 7 Session 1.3

▲ Student Activity Book, p. 8

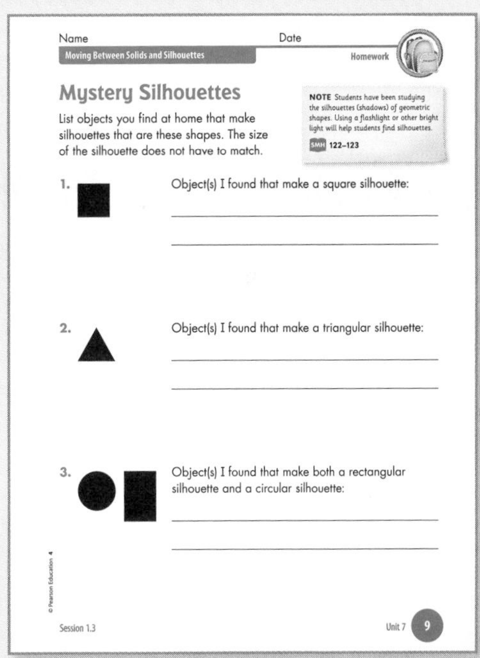

Name Date

Moving Between Solids and Silhouettes — Homework

Mystery Silhouettes

NOTE Students have been studying the silhouettes (shadows) of geometric shapes. Using a flashlight or other bright light will help students find silhouettes. SMH 122–123

List objects you find at home that make silhouettes that are these shapes. The size of the silhouette does not have to match.

1. Object(s) I found that make a square silhouette:

2. Object(s) I found that make a triangular silhouette:

3. Object(s) I found that make both a rectangular silhouette and a circular silhouette:

© Pearson Education 4

Session 1.3 Unit 7 9

▲ Student Activity Book, p. 9

Assessment: Match the Silhouettes

Math Focus Points

- Understanding how 3-D solids project silhouettes with 2-D shapes (for example, how a cone can produce both triangular and circular silhouettes)
- Visualizing what 3-D figures look like from different perspectives

Today's Plan			Materials
1	ACTIVITY **What Can You See from Here?**	50 MIN GROUPS	• *Student Activity Book,* pp. 11–12 • Geometric solids; toy figures
2	ASSESSMENT ACTIVITY **Match the Silhouettes**	10 MIN INDIVIDUALS	• *Student Activity Book,* p. 13 • M14*
3	SESSION FOLLOW-UP **Daily Practice and Homework**		• *Student Activity Book,* pp. 14–15 • *Student Math Handbook,* pp. 122–123

*See *Materials to Prepare,* p. 21.

Ten-Minute Math

Quick Images: 3-D **Show Images 3 and 4 from *Quick Images: 3-D* (T74), and follow the procedure for the basic routine. For each image, students discuss how they built their structures, focusing on the relationship between the two images. Ask questions such as:**

- How did you remember the parts of the image?
- Are there any parts of these two images that are the same?
- Was there anything about Image 3 that helped you build Image 4?

ACTIVITY

What Can You See from Here?

50 MIN GROUPS

Continue the activity from Session 1.3, using *Student Activity Book* pages 11 and 12. Students will have to rebuild the landscape on their sheets of paper. When you get to page 11, challenge students to figure out the answers without first building the landscape. They can then check their answers by building the landscape.

As you circulate, look for instances of disagreement or uncertainty among students. Have brief small-group or whole-class discussions about these specific questions.

Challenge students to "see" the 2-D landscape before "building" 3-D structures.

The following chart lists reasonable answers. Let students decide which answers they will accept as correct; students sometimes make a good case for answers that are not listed below. Watch for and encourage good reasoning as students discuss how 2-D silhouettes represent 3-D shapes.①

Landscape 2	Landscape 3
Pair 1: A, F	Pair 1: D
Pair 2: E	Pair 2: H
Pair 3: C	Pair 3: C, G

Professional Development

① **Dialogue Box:** Good Thinking Does Not Always Result in Correct Answers, p. 113

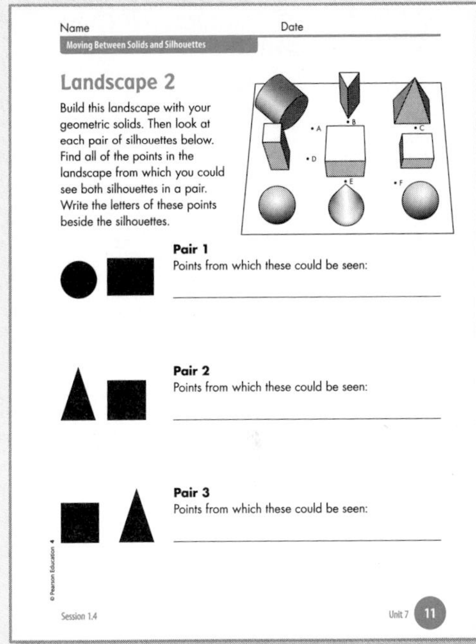

Name Date

Moving Between Solids and Silhouettes

Landscape 2

Build this landscape with your geometric solids. Then look at each pair of silhouettes below. Find all of the points in the landscape from which you could see both silhouettes in a pair. Write the letters of these points beside the silhouettes.

Pair 1
Points from which these could be seen:

Pair 2
Points from which these could be seen:

Pair 3
Points from which these could be seen:

© Pearson Education 4

Session 1.4 Unit 7 11

▲ Student Activity Book, p. 11

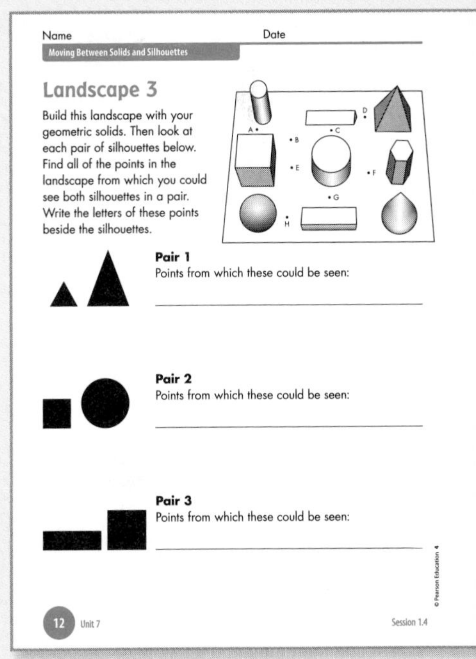

Name Date

Moving Between Solids and Silhouettes

Landscape 3

Build this landscape with your geometric solids. Then look at each pair of silhouettes below. Find all of the points in the landscape from which you could see both silhouettes in a pair. Write the letters of these points beside the silhouettes.

Pair 1
Points from which these could be seen:

Pair 2
Points from which these could be seen:

Pair 3
Points from which these could be seen:

© Pearson Education 4

12 Unit 7 Session 1.4

▲ Student Activity Book, p. 12

Professional Development

❷ **Teacher Note:** Assessment: Match the Silhouettes, p. 99

Name Date

Moving Between Solids and Silhouettes

Landscapes Challenge

Look at this pair of silhouettes. Find all of the points in the three geometric landscapes from which these two silhouettes could be seen. Write the letters of these points from *Student Activity Book* pages 7, 11, and 12.

These could be seen from the following points:

In Landscape 1:

In Landscape 2:

In Landscape 3:

© Pearson Education 4

Session 1.4 Unit 7 13

▲ Student Activity Book, p. 13

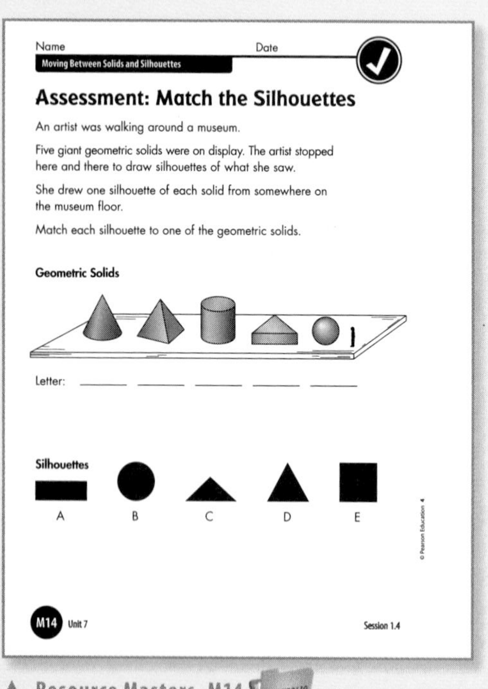

Name Date

Moving Between Solids and Silhouettes

Assessment: Match the Silhouettes

An artist was walking around a museum.

Five giant geometric solids were on display. The artist stopped here and there to draw silhouettes of what she saw.

She drew one silhouette of each solid from somewhere on the museum floor.

Match each silhouette to one of the geometric solids.

Geometric Solids

Letter: ____ ____ ____ ____ ____

Silhouettes

A B C D E

© Pearson Education 4

M14 Unit 7 Session 1.4

▲ Resource Masters, M14 PORTFOLIO

ONGOING ASSESSMENT: Observing Students at Work

Students match pairs of silhouettes to geometric solids.

- **How do students decide on their answers?** Do they crouch down in order to see from the same perspective as the toy figure? How easily are students able to visualize the silhouette?
- **What names are students using for the solids?** Are they using mathematical names or informal names?

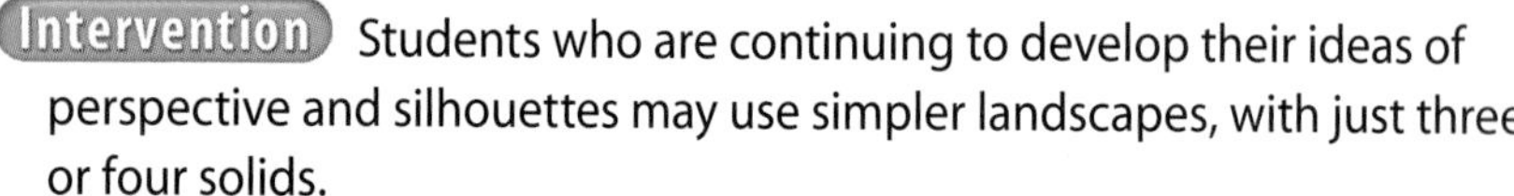

DIFFERENTIATION: Supporting the Range of Learners

Intervention Students who are continuing to develop their ideas of perspective and silhouettes may use simpler landscapes, with just three or four solids.

Extension Students who seem to solve these problems easily may find *Student Activity Book* page 13 more challenging. Because they are asked to refer to three of the landscapes from pages 7, 11, and 12, encourage students to answer by looking only at the diagrams, not by rebuilding the landscapes. Reasonable answers for page 13 are Landscape 1—B, C, F; Landscape 2—B, D; Landscape 3—A, B, F.

10 MIN INDIVIDUALS

ASSESSMENT ACTIVITY

2 Match the Silhouettes

For the last 10 minutes or so of this session, have students complete individually Assessment: Match the Silhouettes (M14). Students match the silhouette to a picture of the geometric solid that made it.❷

This assessment addresses Benchmark 1: Identifying 2-dimensional silhouettes of 3-dimensional solids (e.g., a cone can project a triangular silhouette).

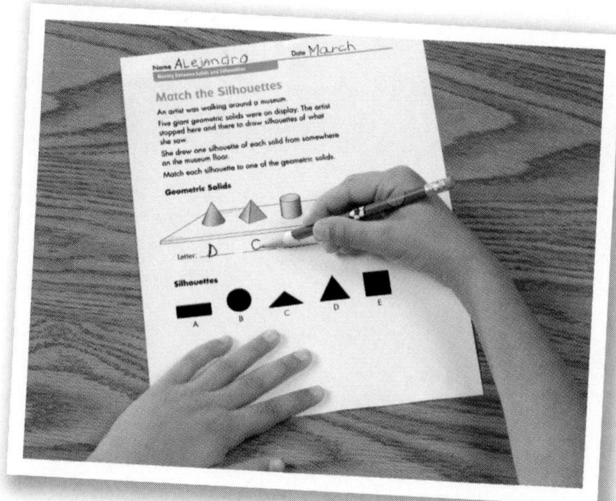

Match the Silhouettes *assesses students' ability to match silhouette to solid.*

Note that the solids in the picture on this page do not correspond to the set of solids the class has been using. The cone, square pyramid, and large cylinder are different sizes and heights, and the triangular prism shown on the page is quite different from the one in the set. However, students should be allowed to use the solids to help them identify silhouettes. If they do use the solids, students should indicate this on their pages.

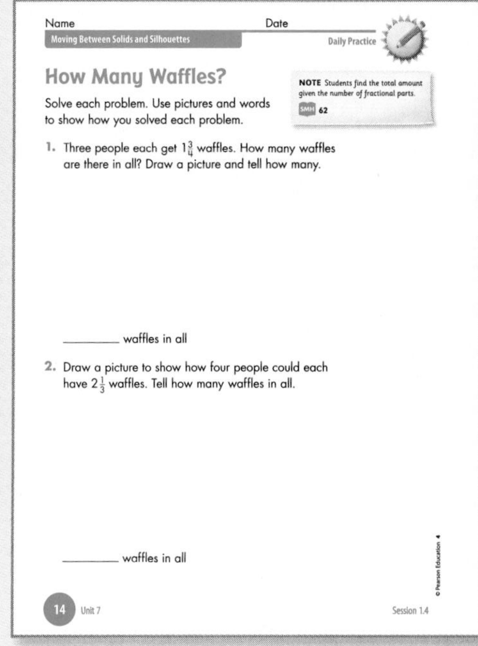

Name Date

Moving Between Solids and Silhouettes — Daily Practice

How Many Waffles?

Solve each problem. Use pictures and words to show how you solved each problem.

NOTE Students find the total amount given the number of fractional parts. SMH 62

1. Three people each get $1\frac{3}{4}$ waffles. How many waffles are there in all? Draw a picture and tell how many.

_______ waffles in all

2. Draw a picture to show how four people could each have $2\frac{1}{3}$ waffles. Tell how many waffles in all.

_______ waffles in all

14 Unit 7 Session 1.4

© Pearson Education 4

▲ Student Activity Book, p. 14

SESSION FOLLOW-UP
3 Daily Practice and Homework

Daily Practice: For ongoing review, have students complete *Student Activity Book* page 14.

Homework: Students compare different fractions on *Student Activity Book* page 15.

Student Math Handbook: Students and families may use *Student Math Handbook* pages 122–123 for reference and review. See pages 119–121 in the back of this unit.

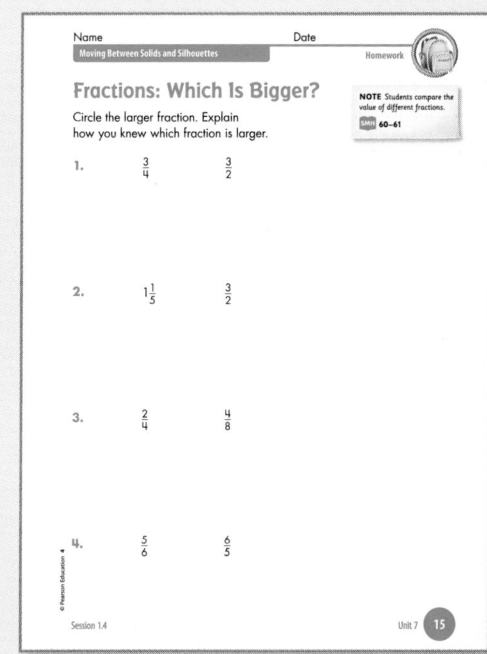

Name Date

Moving Between Solids and Silhouettes — Homework

Fractions: Which Is Bigger?

Circle the larger fraction. Explain how you knew which fraction is larger.

NOTE Students compare the value of different fractions. SMH 60–61

1. $\frac{3}{4}$ $\frac{3}{2}$

2. $1\frac{1}{5}$ $\frac{3}{2}$

3. $\frac{2}{4}$ $\frac{4}{8}$

4. $\frac{5}{6}$ $\frac{6}{5}$

© Pearson Education 4

Session 1.4 Unit 7 15

▲ Student Activity Book, p. 15

INVESTIGATION 2

Mathematical Emphases

Features of Shape Translating between 2-dimensional and 3-dimensional shapes

Math Focus Points

- Visualizing what 3-D figures look like from different perspectives
- Recognizing how components of 3-D cube buildings come together to form the whole building
- Drawing silhouettes of 3-D cube buildings from different perspectives
- Integrating different silhouettes of an object, both to form a mental model and to build the whole object

Volume Structuring rectangular prisms and determining their volume

Math Focus Points

- Finding the number of cubes (volume) that will fit into the box made by a given pattern

Making and Visualizing Cube Buildings

Session	Student Activity Book	Student Math Handbook	Professional Development: Read Ahead of Time
SESSION 2.1 p. 48 **Building with Cubes** Using 2-D drawings, students construct 3-D buildings and discuss strategies for building them. Students also discuss the number of cubes—or volume—of these buildings.	17–20	124	• **Teacher Note:** Interpreting 2-D Diagrams of 3-D Shapes, p. 100
SESSION 2.2 p. 55 **Drawing Silhouettes of Cube Buildings** Students construct cube buildings and draw silhouettes showing 3 different perspectives (top, front, and right sides) of each structure.	21–25	124	• **Teacher Note:** Staying Properly Oriented, p. 101 • **Dialogue Box:** Describing Our Building Silhouettes, p. 115
SESSION 2.3 p. 60 **Drawing Before Building** Students examine drawings of cube buildings and draw silhouettes showing 3 different perspectives (top, front, and right sides) of each structure. They then construct the building and compare the 3-D shape with their 2-D drawing.	22–23, 27–29	124	
SESSION 2.4 p. 64 **Integrating Views to Make a Cube Building** Students are given the front, top, and right-side silhouettes and construct the matching cube buildings.	30–32	124	• **Teacher Note:** Integrating Three Views: How Students Try to Do It, p. 102
SESSION 2.5 p. 69 **Assessment: Drawing Silhouettes** Given a map of a cube city with the height of each building marked, students determine the locations from which different silhouettes of the city can be seen. Then they build the city to check. They are assessed on their ability to draw silhouettes of cube buildings.	33–34	124	

Ten-Minute Math See page 16 for an overview.

Practicing Place Value

- No materials needed

Quick Images

- T74–T75, *Quick Images: 3-D*
- Connecting cubes (15–20 per student)

Materials to Gather	Materials to Prepare
• **Connecting cubes** (70 per student pair)	
• **T77, Drawing Silhouettes: An Introduction** • **Connecting cubes** (30 per student)	
• **Connecting cubes** (30 per student)	
• **Connecting cubes** (30 per student)	
• **Connecting cubes** (30 per student)	• **M16–M17, Assessment: Drawing Silhouettes** Make copies. (1 per student) • **M18, Assessment Checklist: Drawing Silhouettes** Make copies. (1 per 10 students)

Overhead Transparency   Checklist Available

Building with Cubes

Math Focus Points

- Recognizing how components of 3-D cube buildings come together to form the whole building
- Finding the volume of cube buildings

Vocabulary

volume

Today's Plan			Materials
1 ACTIVITY **Making Cube Buildings**	30 MIN	PAIRS	• *Student Activity Book,* pp. 17–18 • Connecting cubes
2 DISCUSSION **Building Strategies**	10 MIN	CLASS	• *Student Activity Book,* pp. 17–18 • Connecting cubes
3 ACTIVITY **How Many Cubes?**	20 MIN	CLASS	• *Student Activity Book,* pp. 17–18 • Connecting cubes
4 SESSION FOLLOW-UP **Daily Practice and Homework**			• *Student Activity Book,* pp. 19–20 • *Student Math Handbook,* p. 124

Ten-Minute Math

Quick Images: 3-D Show Images 5 and 6 from *Quick Images: 3-D* (T74), and follow the procedure for the basic routine. For each image, students discuss how they built their structures, focusing on the relationship between the two images. Ask questions such as:

- How did you remember the parts of the image?
- Are there any parts of these two images that are the same?
- Was there anything about Image 5 that helped you build Image 6?

1 ACTIVITY
Making Cube Buildings

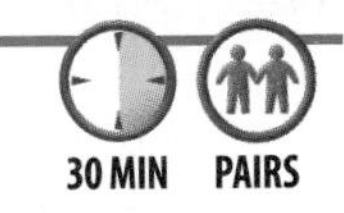

Provide 70 connecting cubes for each pair of students. Direct students' attention to Building 1 from *Student Activity Book* page 17. Explain that each student in a pair should make a version of this building with cubes. Then students can compare their buildings.

When they compare their buildings, students should hold them in the position seen in the drawing. That is, they should be looking at the front, right edge, not at the front (the shaded part), side, or top.

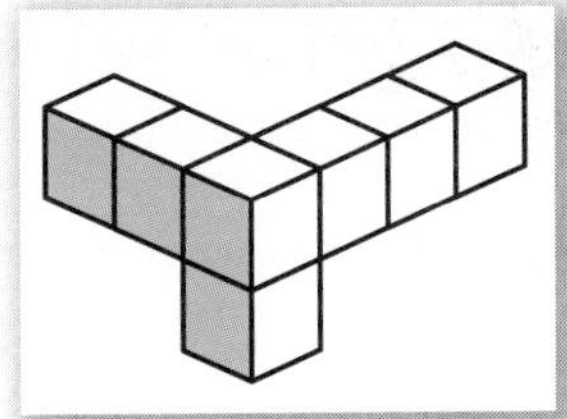

After Building 1 is complete, illustrate (or have students illustrate) this viewing position by standing at the front of the room with your back to the class and with your building positioned so that you are looking at the correct edge. This idea of having the same perspective and discussing the front, top, and side is used throughout this Investigation.

Students can demonstrate that they understand how to construct cube buildings by showing the class.

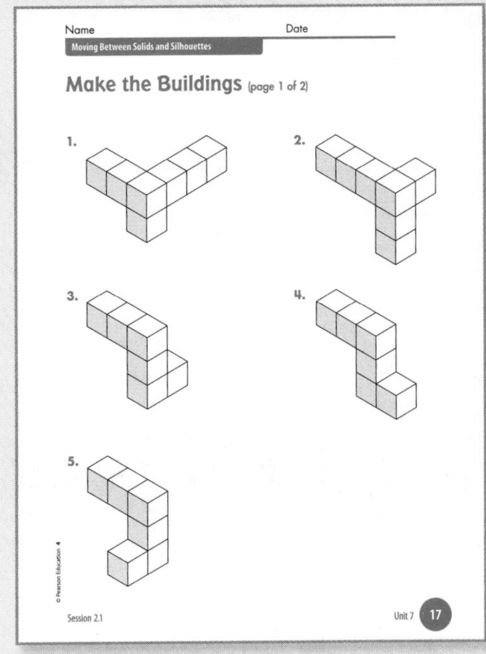

Name Date

Moving Between Solids and Silhouettes

Make the Buildings (page 1 of 2)

1.

2.

3.

4.

5.

© Pearson Education 4

Session 2.1 Unit 7 17

▲ **Student Activity Book, p. 17**

Professional Development

① **Teacher Note:** Interpreting 2-D Diagrams of 3-D Shapes, p. 100

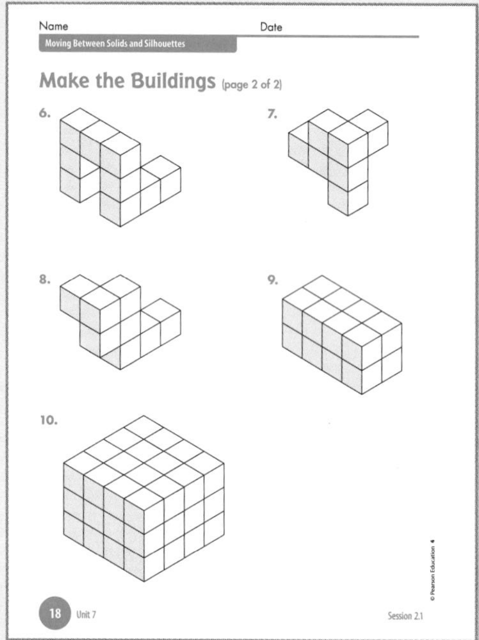
Name Date

Moving Between Solids and Silhouettes

Make the Buildings (page 2 of 2)

6.

7.

8.

9.

10.

18 Unit 7 Session 2.1

© Pearson Education 4

▲ Student Activity Book, p. 18

Ask students to describe their strategies for completing Building 1 and to explain how they determined whether their buildings were correct.

Instruct students to complete the buildings shown in drawings 2–8 on *Student Activity Book* pages 17–18. Ask them to use a different set of cubes for each building and to keep all their buildings together. This will give you an opportunity to inspect the results. As they work, encourage students to compare their buildings, both with the drawings and with buildings made by their classmates.①

Circulate among students, stopping here and there to point to a cube in a building and ask the student to show you that cube in the drawing. Such questions help you assess students' interpretations of the cube drawings and their ability to put together the buildings shown.

ONGOING ASSESSMENT: Observing Students at Work

Students build 3-D shapes from 2-D drawings.

- **Are students able to construct the buildings correctly?** Are they using the correct perspective?
- **When asked to, can students establish a correspondence between parts of the pictures and parts of the buildings?**
- **Are students using mathematical vocabulary to describe their buildings?**

DIFFERENTIATION: Supporting the Range of Learners

Intervention When constructing Building 3, many students have trouble correctly placing the cube for the front right leg. Instead they make Buildings 4 or 5. These students are having difficulty interpreting the drawings; however, their confusion usually clears up as they go on to build all three.

DISCUSSION

2 Building Strategies

Math Focus Points for Discussion

- Recognizing how components of 3-D cube buildings come together to form the whole building

Discuss as a class the strategies students used to construct their buildings, asking them to compare the buildings shown in different drawings.❷ Ask the following questions:

- How are Buildings 1 and 2 related? (They are pictures of the same cube arrangement from different perspectives.)
- How are buildings 3, 4, and 5 the same or different? (Six of the cubes are the same; the difference is the placement of the seventh cube.)
- How many cubes did you use to make Building 6? (Accept reasonable answers.)

From the drawing of Building 6, it is not clear whether there are cubes in the back that are obscured by the front cubes. Consequently, some students extend the back left leg when they construct Building 6 with cubes. Here, as in other instances in this Investigation, there is more than one correct building depending on how students interpret the drawing of the cube building.

As students discuss their interpretations of the drawings, they start to develop the language and concepts needed to communicate spatial information.

Differentiation

❷ **English Language Leaners** To continue helping English Language Learners acquire the vocabulary needed to describe their own strategies, you can model the strategies that other students describe or ask other students to do themselves. By seeing the strategies as they are being described, English Language Learners will better understand the expressions students use.

Teaching Note

❸ **Using Mathematical Vocabulary** As students talk about the buildings and solids in this unit, they may use their own words (rather than standard terminology) to describe the objects and their parts. For example, they often use the word "sides" instead of "faces." Introduce and use the standard terms as they fit into the discussion. Encourage students to use the standard terms consistently because it helps them communicate clearly.

20 MIN CLASS

ACTIVITY

3 How Many Cubes?

Introduce volume to students by asking them to compare Buildings 1–8 on *Student Activity Book* pages 17–18.

One way that we can measure 3-dimensional objects is by thinking about how much space they fill, or their **volume**. Volume is measured in cubic units, such as cubic inches, cubic feet, or cubic meters. For now we'll just talk about how many cubes it takes to make these buildings.

Which building is biggest; that is, which uses the most cubes?

Which building is smallest, or uses the fewest cubes?

Which is bigger: Building 6 or Building 8? Building 2 or Building 8?

Ask students for their predictions of how many cubes it would take to make Buildings 9 and 10. Ask how they made their predictions. Some students use a layer approach. That is, they determine how many cubes are in a vertical or horizontal layer and how many layers there are and then add or multiply to find the total. Other students make incorrect predictions by counting only those cubes that are visible on the three exposed sides or by counting visible faces rather than cubes.

After discussing their predictions, have students make Buildings 9 and 10 with cubes to check their answers. (To have enough cubes, they will have to take apart Buildings 1–8.)

Discuss the strategies that students used to determine numbers of cubes in the buildings. Let students use any strategy that enables them to count accurately. This discussion continues the focus from Grade 3, in which students thought about the volume of prisms by focusing on the structure of cubes making the prism. Students focus specifically on finding volume in Investigation 3.❸

ONGOING ASSESSMENT: Observing Students at Work

Students build rectangular prisms and determine their volume.

- **How do students determine volume?** Do they use layers? Do they multiply (or add) the number of cubes in 1 layer by the number of layers in the rectangular prism?
- **Do students include the "internal" cubes in their count or count only those cubes they can see (resulting in an incorrect answer)?**

DIFFERENTIATION: Supporting the Range of Learners

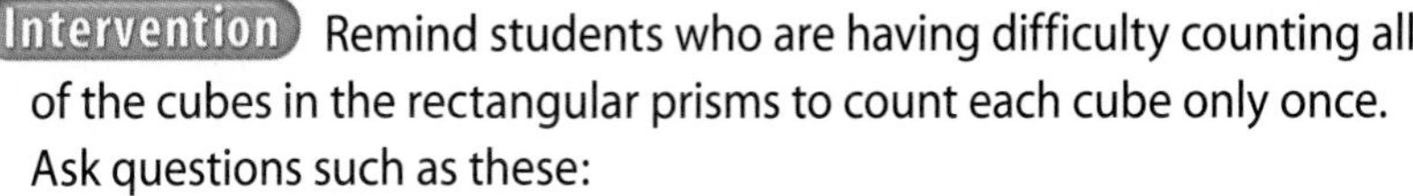

Intervention Remind students who are having difficulty counting all of the cubes in the rectangular prisms to count each cube only once. Ask questions such as these:

- Are there any cubes you may have counted more than once?
- Are there any cubes that are part of more than 1 row or column?
- Are you counting cubes that you can't see?

Some students make the same errors when counting cubes in the actual 3-D buildings as they do when counting them in the drawings. In fact, for some students, determining the number of cubes in rectangular prisms such as Buildings 9 and 10 is a very difficult and confusing problem. The only way these students will be convinced of the correct total is to take the buildings apart and count the cubes 1 by 1.

ELL You can activate English Language Learners' prior knowledge by comparing volume to something similiar and familiar: area. Point at objects as you are discussing them.

Remember when we wanted to find out how much space this shape covered? We figured out *area* in *square units*. We counted the squares that *covered* the flat shape. Now we want to find out how many cubes *fill up* or *fit in* the whole building, or how many cubes it takes to make the building. This measurement is called *volume*, and it's measured in *cubic units*.

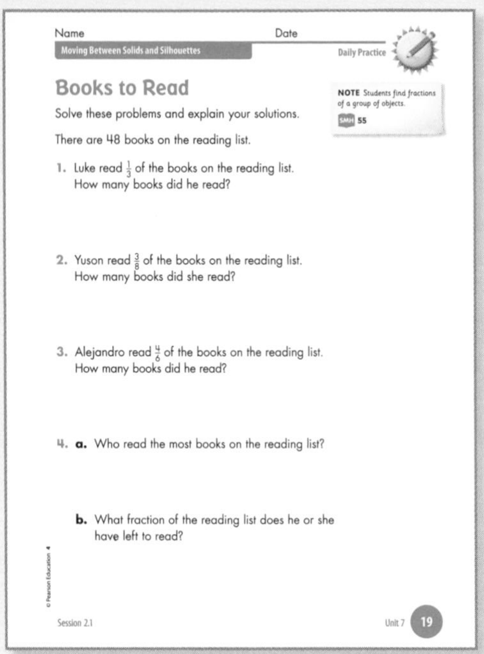

Name Date

Moving Between Solids and Silhouettes — Daily Practice

Books to Read

NOTE Students find fractions of a group of objects. SMH 55

Solve these problems and explain your solutions.

There are 48 books on the reading list.

1. Luke read $\frac{1}{3}$ of the books on the reading list. How many books did he read?
2. Yuson read $\frac{3}{8}$ of the books on the reading list. How many books did she read?
3. Alejandro read $\frac{4}{6}$ of the books on the reading list. How many books did he read?
4. **a.** Who read the most books on the reading list?

   b. What fraction of the reading list does he or she have left to read?

© Pearson Education 4

Session 2.1 Unit 7 19

▲ Student Activity Book, p. 19

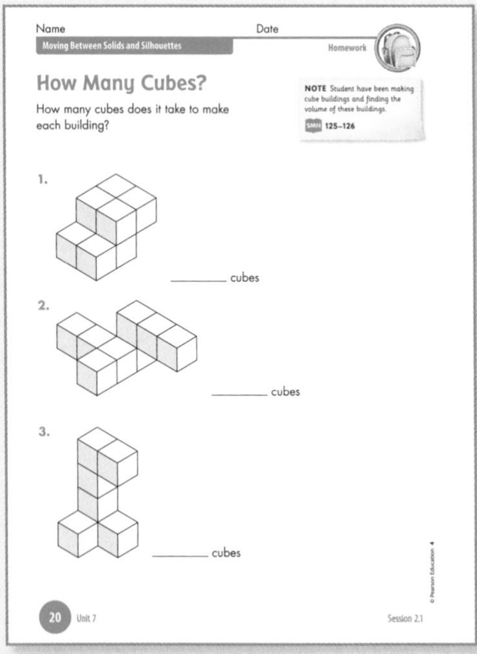

Name Date

Moving Between Solids and Silhouettes — Homework

How Many Cubes?

NOTE Students have been making cube buildings and finding the volume of these buildings. SMH 125–126

How many cubes does it take to make each building?

1. ______ cubes
2. ______ cubes
3. ______ cubes

© Pearson Education 4

20 Unit 7 Session 2.1

▲ Student Activity Book, p. 20

SESSION FOLLOW-UP

4 Daily Practice and Homework

Daily Practice: For ongoing review, have students complete *Student Activity Book* page 19.

Homework: Students find the volume of cube buildings on *Student Activity Book* page 20.

Student Math Handbook: Students and families may use *Student Math Handbook* page 124 for reference and review. See pages 119–121 in the back of this unit.

Drawing Silhouettes of Cube Buildings

Math Focus Points

- Drawing silhouettes of 3-D cube buildings from different perspectives

Today's Plan		Materials
1 ACTIVITY **Introducing Different Silhouettes**	20 MIN CLASS	• *Student Activity Book,* p. 21 • T77 • Connecting cubes
2 ACTIVITY **Drawing All Three Views**	25 MIN INDIVIDUALS PAIRS	• *Student Activity Book,* pp. 22–23 • Connecting cubes
3 DISCUSSION **Describing Our Silhouettes**	15 MIN CLASS	• *Student Activity Book,* p. 22
4 SESSION FOLLOW-UP **Daily Practice and Homework**		• *Student Activity Book,* pp. 24–25 • *Student Math Handbook,* p. 124

Ten-Minute Math

Practicing Place Value Say "sixty-seven and two tenths," and ask students to write the number. Make sure that all students can read, write, and say this number correctly. Ask students to solve these problems mentally, if possible:

- What is 67.2 + 0.1?
- 67.2 + 0.5?
- 67.2 − 10?
- 67.2 − 20?

Write each answer on the board. Ask students to compare each sum and difference with 67.2. Which places have the same digits? Which do not? Why? If time remains, pose additional similar problems with the number: 89.59 and 56.41.

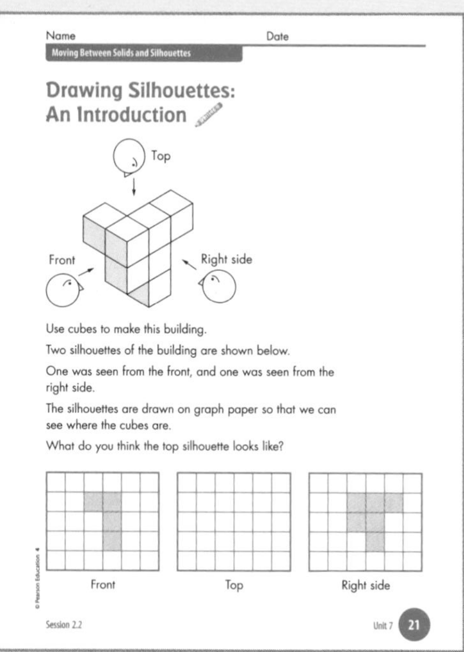
Name Date

Moving Between Solids and Silhouettes

Drawing Silhouettes: An Introduction

Top

Front

Right side

Use cubes to make this building.

Two silhouettes of the building are shown below.

One was seen from the front, and one was seen from the right side.

The silhouettes are drawn on graph paper so that we can see where the cubes are.

What do you think the top silhouette looks like?

Front Top Right side

Session 2.2 Unit 7 21

▲ Student Activity Book, p. 21

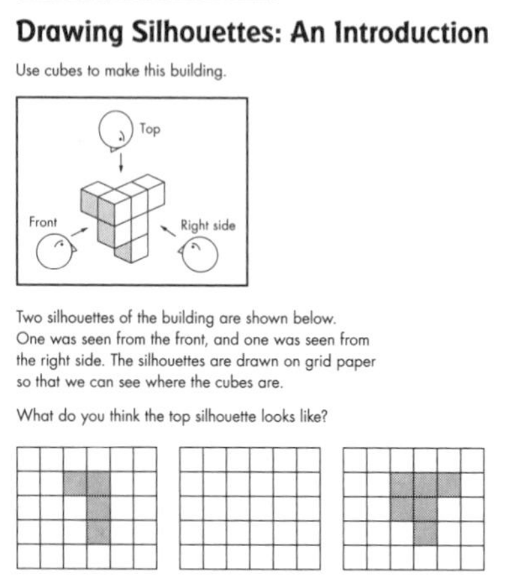
Moving Between Solids and Silhouettes

Drawing Silhouettes: An Introduction

Use cubes to make this building.

Top

Front

Right side

Two silhouettes of the building are shown below. One was seen from the front, and one was seen from the right side. The silhouettes are drawn on grid paper so that we can see where the cubes are.

What do you think the top silhouette looks like?

Front Top Right side

T77

▲ Transparencies, T77

1 ACTIVITY

20 MIN CLASS

Introducing Different Silhouettes

Students use cubes to make the building shown on *Student Activity Book* page 21. When every student is done making the building, display Drawing Silhouettes: An Introduction (T77). Point out that each square on the grids corresponds to one cube.

Invite a volunteer to come to the front of the classroom and show the class the front of this cube building. Then place the student's building on the overhead glass so that the front of the building is facing upward, directly under the mirror (see the photo below). Support the building with your hand as necessary. Repeat this procedure for the silhouette of the right side.

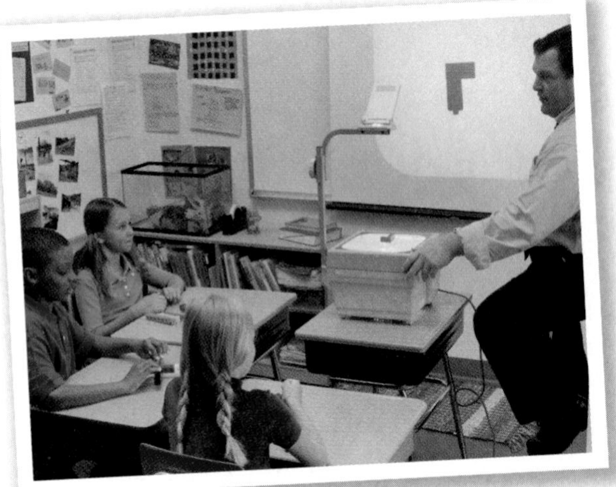

Students draw silhouettes of their cube buildings and verify silhouettes on the overhead.

Have students position their buildings exactly as shown at the top of *Student Activity Book* page 21. Ask students to draw the silhouette seen by looking down at the top of the building in the blank grid. Look for the four positions on the next page and recreate them on the board or overhead for class discussion.

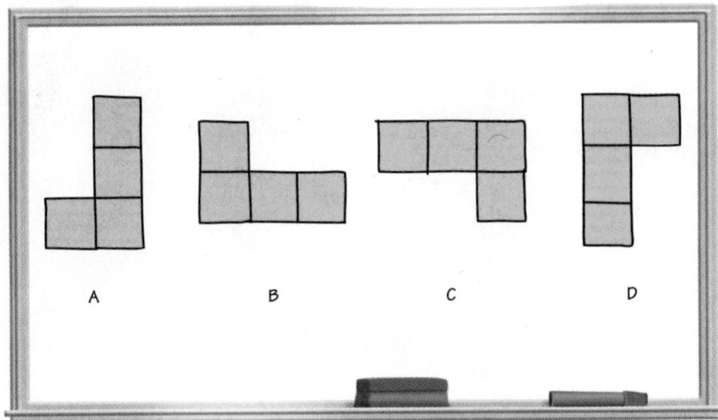

Ask students how these four silhouettes are different and how they are the same. *(They have the same number of cubes and configuration but are drawn from different perspectives.)* You can demonstrate on the overhead—by turning the building—that each is a silhouette seen from a different side of the same building.

In diagrams like this, to avoid confusion, we will draw the top silhouette as seen from the front side. See, for example, the silhouette labeled "A."

ACTIVITY

2 Drawing All Three Views

Students first use the connecting cubes to make some of the cube buildings shown on *Student Activity Book* pages 22–23. Then they draw front, top, and right-side silhouettes. Remind students to follow the standard practice of drawing the top as viewed from the front. Pairs of students should compare answers and discuss any disagreements.[1]

Professional Development

[1] **Teacher Note:** Staying Properly Oriented, p. 101

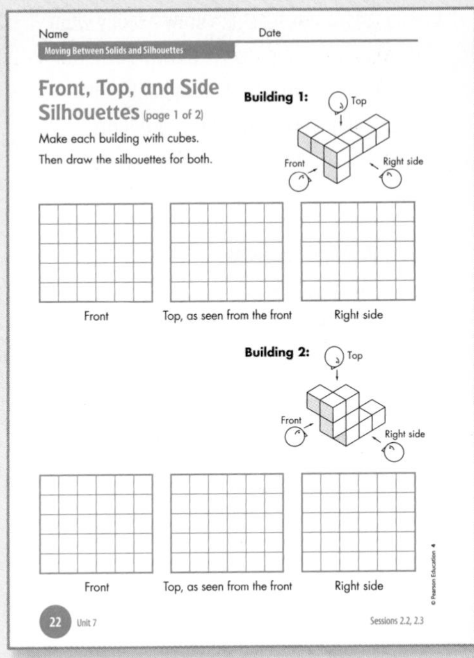

Name Date

Moving Between Solids and Silhouettes

Front, Top, and Side Silhouettes (page 1 of 2)

Make each building with cubes.
Then draw the silhouettes for both.

Building 1:

Front | Top, as seen from the front | Right side

Building 2:

Front | Top, as seen from the front | Right side

22 Unit 7 Sessions 2.2, 2.3

▲ Student Activity Book, p. 22

Teaching Note

② Helping Students Make Precise Descriptions As students describe how they drew the silhouettes, many teachers draw exactly what students say (as opposed to drawing what they know students are trying to say) and make intentional mistakes. This helps students become more precise in their descriptions.

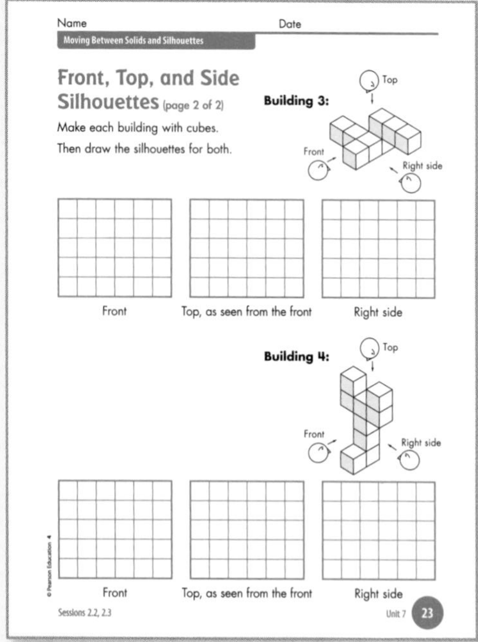

Name　　　　Date

Moving Between Solids and Silhouettes

Front, Top, and Side Silhouettes (page 2 of 2)

Make each building with cubes.
Then draw the silhouettes for both.

Building 3:

Top
Front
Right side

Front　　Top, as seen from the front　　Right side

Building 4:

Top
Front
Right side

Front　　Top, as seen from the front　　Right side

© Pearson Education 4

Sessions 2.2, 2.3　　Unit 7　23

▲ Student Activity Book, p. 23

By comparing and discussing their answers, students learn to correct their own mistakes.

Students need not complete both pages 22 and 23; they will have additional time in Session 2.3. Alert students that at the end of this session, the whole class will discuss the solution to Building 2.

ONGOING ASSESSMENT: Observing Students at Work

Students draw top, front, and right-side silhouettes of cube buildings.

- **Are students drawing all the cubes for a given silhouette?**
- **Are students able to draw the "recessed" cubes—that is, cubes that are not on the same plane?**
- **Are students able to stay properly oriented to the building, and do they use the same position to draw each of the silhouettes?**

DISCUSSION

Describing Our Silhouettes

Math Focus Points for Discussion

- Drawing silhouettes of 3-D cube buildings from different perspectives

Use Building 2 on *Student Activity Book* page 22 as the focus for this discussion. Ask students how they are visualizing the front silhouette of the figure.❷ Focus on two difficulties that commonly arise:

- Drawing the top silhouette from a perspective other than the front
- Failing to draw recessed cubes

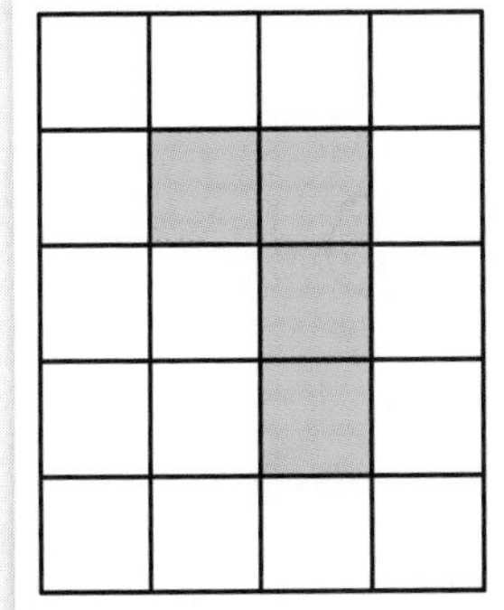

Some disagreements may be resolved by positioning cube buildings on the overhead to show the silhouette.❸ Although students are expected to present logical, verbal explanations about which cubes (including recessed cubes) appear in a silhouette, some students will be convinced only by actually seeing the silhouette.

SESSION FOLLOW-UP

Daily Practice and Homework

Daily Practice: For ongoing review, have students complete *Student Activity Book* page 24.

Homework: Have students compare decimals on *Student Activity Book* page 25.

Student Math Handbook: Students and families may use *Student Math Handbook* page 124 for reference and review. See pages 119–121 in the back of this unit.

Professional Development

❸ **Dialogue Box:** Describing Our Building Silhouettes, p. 115

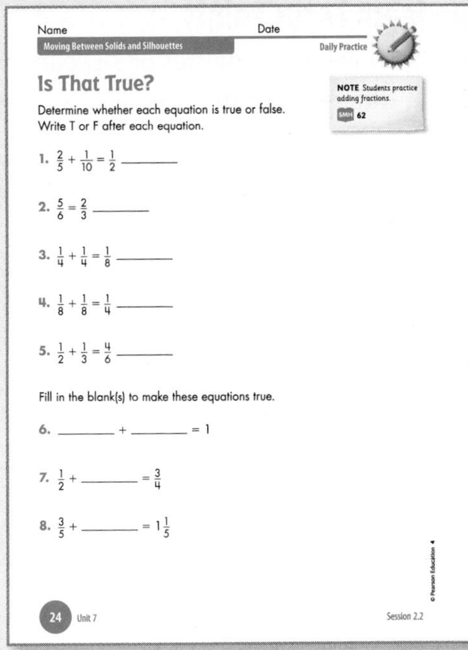

Name Date

Moving Between Solids and Silhouettes — Daily Practice

Is That True?

NOTE Students practice adding fractions. SMH 62

Determine whether each equation is true or false. Write T or F after each equation.

1. $\frac{2}{5} + \frac{1}{10} = \frac{1}{2}$ ______
2. $\frac{5}{6} = \frac{2}{3}$ ______
3. $\frac{1}{4} + \frac{1}{4} = \frac{1}{8}$ ______
4. $\frac{1}{8} + \frac{1}{8} = \frac{1}{4}$ ______
5. $\frac{1}{2} + \frac{1}{3} = \frac{4}{6}$ ______

Fill in the blank(s) to make these equations true.

6. ______ + ______ = 1
7. $\frac{1}{2}$ + ______ = $\frac{3}{4}$
8. $\frac{3}{5}$ + ______ = $1\frac{1}{5}$

© Pearson Education 4

24 Unit 7 Session 2.2

▲ Student Activity Book, p. 24

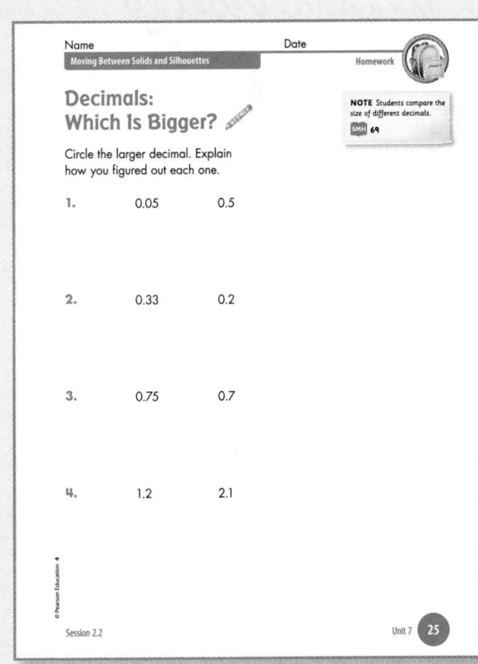

Name Date

Moving Between Solids and Silhouettes — Homework

Decimals: Which Is Bigger?

NOTE Students compare the size of different decimals. SMH 69

Circle the larger decimal. Explain how you figured out each one.

1. 0.05 0.5
2. 0.33 0.2
3. 0.75 0.7
4. 1.2 2.1

© Pearson Education 4

Session 2.2 Unit 7 25

▲ Student Activity Book, p. 25

SESSION 2.3

Drawing Before Building

Math Focus Points

- Drawing silhouettes of 3-D cube buildings from different perspectives

Today's Plan		Materials
1 ACTIVITY **Drawing Before Building**	15 MIN INDIVIDUALS	• *Student Activity Book,* p. 27 • Connecting cubes
2 DISCUSSION **Strategies for Drawing**	10 MIN CLASS	• *Student Activity Book,* p. 27
3 ACTIVITY **Silhouettes of Buildings**	35 MIN INDIVIDUALS	• *Student Activity Book,* pp. 22–23 (from Session 2.2) • *Student Activity Book,* p. 28 • Connecting cubes
4 SESSION FOLLOW-UP **Daily Practice**		• *Student Activity Book,* p. 29 • *Student Math Handbook,* p. 124

Ten-Minute Math

Practicing Place Value Write 75.12 on the board and have students practice saying it. Let students know that this number is commonly read both as "seventy-five and twelve hundredths" and "seventy-five point twelve". Make sure all students can read, write, and say this number correctly.

Ask students to solve these problems mentally, if possible:

- What is one tenth more than 75.12?
- What is five tenths more?
- What is five hundredths more?

Write each number on the board. Ask students to compare each sum with 75.12. Which places have the same digits? Which do not? Why? If time remains, pose additional similar problems using these numbers: 123.06 and 48.25.

ACTIVITY

1 Drawing Before Building

15 MIN INDIVIDUALS

Students draw silhouettes before constructing a building, and then they make the building, draw the silhouettes again, and compare silhouettes.

In our last session you drew silhouettes of different perspectives of cube buildings. You're going to do more of that today, but this time you'll draw the silhouettes before you make the building.

Tell students to complete *Student Activity Book* page 27 and then compare their two sets of silhouettes.

This activity helps you informally assess your students' strengths and weaknesses regarding visualization strategies.

ONGOING ASSESSMENT: Observing Students at Work

Students draw silhouettes before making the building. Next, they make the building and draw the silhouettes again, and then they compare the silhouettes.

- **Are students able to draw the silhouettes without making the cube building?**
- **Are students making such errors as interchanging views (drawing the side for the front), not drawing cubes that are recessed, or drawing a top view that is not from the front perspective?**

DIFFERENTIATION: Supporting the Range of Learners

Intervention Students who cannot draw the silhouettes without making the buildings need more experience with drawing the three views from images and then checking their answers by building. The repeated comparisons of their images with the buildings will help them sharpen their visualization skills.

Students who cannot draw the correct silhouettes even after making the buildings probably need more experience with making cube buildings and drawing the views.

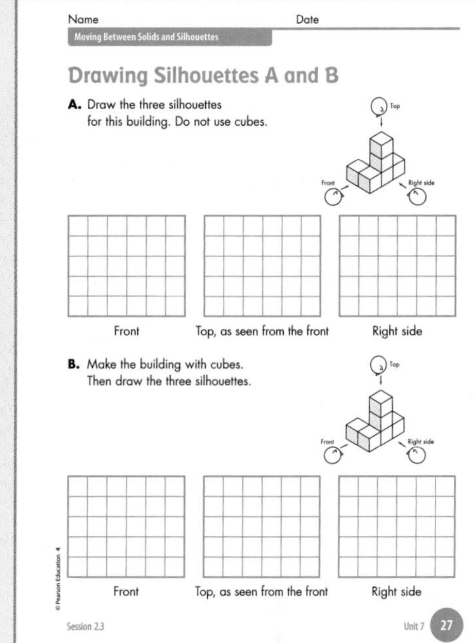

Name Date

Moving Between Solids and Silhouettes

Drawing Silhouettes A and B

A. Draw the three silhouettes for this building. Do not use cubes.

Front | Top, as seen from the front | Right side

B. Make the building with cubes. Then draw the three silhouettes.

Front | Top, as seen from the front | Right side

© Pearson Education 4

Session 2.3 Unit 7 27

▲ Student Activity Book, p. 27

Extension Students who draw correct silhouettes are developing both good visualization skills and an understanding of how 2-D pictures represent 3-D shapes. These students can be challenged by going back to any previous cube building and drawing three further views: the left side, the back, and the bottom. Students may need to make the building first, and should be encouraged to find the relationships between the views. (The front/back, top/bottom, and right-side/left-side silhouettes are mirror images.)

DISCUSSION

Strategies for Drawing

Math Focus Points for Discussion

- Drawing silhouettes of 3-D cube buildings from different perspectives

Ask students to discuss with a partner the following questions about the cube buildings on *Student Activity Book* page 27:

Are the silhouettes you made for Problem B the same as the ones you made for Problem A? How are they different?

Was it easier to make the silhouettes with or without the actual cube building? Why?

Students might say:

"My silhouettes were different. I keep getting confused because I know there are 6 cubes in the building, so I think at least one of my drawings should have 6 cubes. So I could only get it right after I made the building and checked."

"My silhouettes were different, too. It's the top view—I just can't get it right unless I make the building and can stand over it looking at it."

"Mine were the same. At first I was thinking maybe I just got lucky, but then I decided I'm getting this. I feel pretty confident."

At the end of the brief discussion, ask for volunteers to discuss what it was like for them to complete this task.

ACTIVITY
Silhouettes of Buildings

35 MIN INDIVIDUALS

Students spend the remainder of the session completing *Student Activity Book* pages 22–23 (from Session 2.2) and page 28.

Students work individually to draw and compare silhouettes.

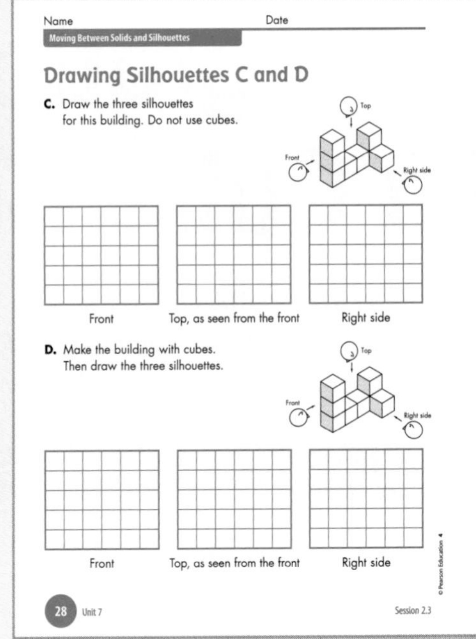

Name Date

Moving Between Solids and Silhouettes

Drawing Silhouettes C and D

C. Draw the three silhouettes for this building. Do not use cubes.

Top

Front

Right side

Front | Top, as seen from the front | Right side

D. Make the building with cubes. Then draw the three silhouettes.

Top

Front

Right side

Front | Top, as seen from the front | Right side

© Pearson Education 4

28 Unit 7 Session 2.3

▲ Student Activity Book, p. 28

SESSION FOLLOW-UP
Daily Practice

Daily Practice: For reinforcement of this unit's content, have students complete *Student Activity Book* page 29.

Student Math Handbook: Students and families may use *Student Math Handbook* page 124 for reference and review. See pages 119–121 in the back of this unit.

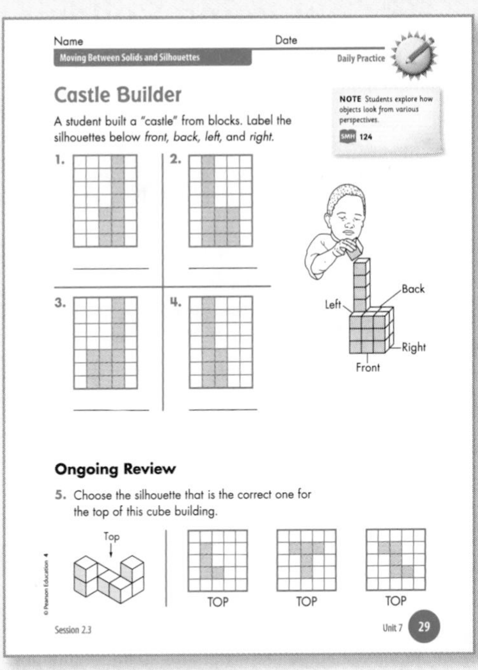

Name Date

Moving Between Solids and Silhouettes

Daily Practice

Castle Builder

NOTE Students explore how objects look from various perspectives.

SMH 124

A student built a "castle" from blocks. Label the silhouettes below *front, back, left,* and *right.*

1. ______ 2. ______

3. ______ 4. ______

Ongoing Review

5. Choose the silhouette that is the correct one for the top of this cube building.

© Pearson Education 4

Session 2.3 Unit 7 29

▲ Student Activity Book, p. 29

Integrating Views to Make a Cube Building

Math Focus Points

- Integrating different silhouettes of an object, both to form a mental model and to build the whole object

Today's Plan			Materials
ACTIVITY **1 Introducing Building from Silhouettes**	15 MIN	INDIVIDUALS	• *Student Activity Book,* p. 30 • Connecting cubes
DISCUSSION **2 Comparing Buildings**	10 MIN	CLASS	• *Student Activity Book,* p. 30
ACTIVITY **3 Building from Silhouettes**	35 MIN	INDIVIDUALS	• *Student Activity Book,* p. 30 • Connecting cubes
SESSION FOLLOW-UP **4 Daily Practice and Homework**			• *Student Activity Book,* pp. 31–32 • *Student Math Handbook,* p. 124

Ten-Minute Math

Quick Images: 3-D Show Images 7 and 8 from *Quick Images: 3-D* (T75), and follow the procedure for the basic routine. For each image, students discuss how they built their structures, including any revisions they made after each viewing. Ask questions such as these:

- How did you remember the parts of the image?
- What did you notice about the relationship of the parts of the image?
- What helped you remember the whole image so that you could build your structure?

ACTIVITY

15 MIN INDIVIDUALS

Introducing Building from Silhouettes

In this activity, students do the reverse of what they have been doing previously.

Today, you are still going to be working on silhouettes, but this time, you will look at the three silhouettes and then make a building that matches all three silhouettes. Construct the building represented in example number 1 on *Student Activity Book* page 30. Then we will have a discussion.

As students work, you are likely to see a variety of solution attempts.

- Some students will make a different building for each of the three silhouettes. Remind them that they are to make one building that will match all three silhouettes.
- Other students will rearrange the cubes in their building for each different silhouette. They show you the front silhouette, but when you ask to see the top silhouette they will move some of the cubes.①

Remind students that they are making only one building and that rearranging the cubes changes the building.

Teaching Note

① **Integrating Views** These are difficult problems that foster the development of an important mental skill: the integration of several separate silhouettes into a single concept of a whole object.

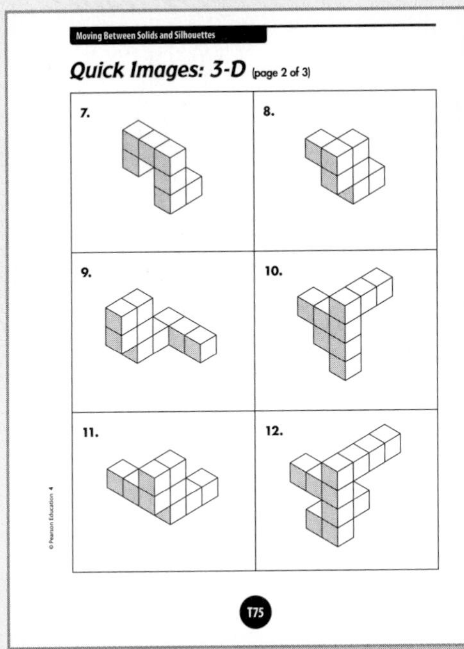

Moving Between Solids and Silhouettes

Quick Images: 3-D (page 2 of 3)

7. 8. 9. 10. 11. 12.

© Pearson Education 4

T75

▲ Transparencies, T75

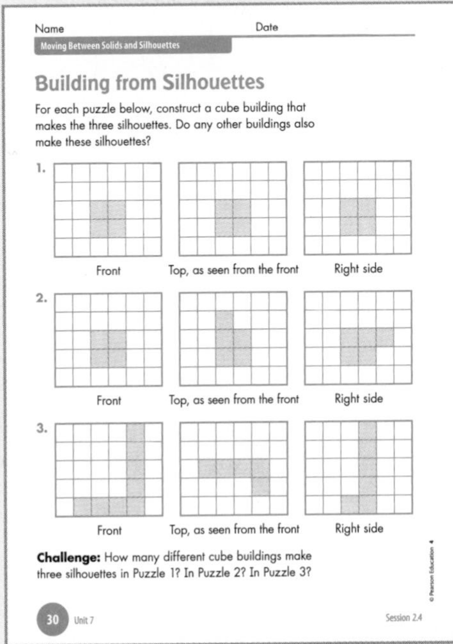

Name Date

Moving Between Solids and Silhouettes

Building from Silhouettes

For each puzzle below, construct a cube building that makes the three silhouettes. Do any other buildings also make these silhouettes?

1. Front | Top, as seen from the front | Right side

2. Front | Top, as seen from the front | Right side

3. Front | Top, as seen from the front | Right side

Challenge: How many different cube buildings make three silhouettes in Puzzle 1? In Puzzle 2? In Puzzle 3?

© Pearson Education 4

30 Unit 7 Session 2.4

▲ Student Activity Book, p. 30 

DISCUSSION

2 Comparing Buildings

Math Focus Points for Discussion

- Integrating different silhouettes of an object, both to form a mental model and to build the whole object

Ask a student to show the building he or she has constructed to the class. Ask whether anyone has a different building. Have students defend their structures, asking them to prove to the class that their building matches all three silhouettes.

Have the overhead projector available so that students can show how their cube buildings match up with the silhouettes.

Have students explain their strategies for constructing the buildings. Ask questions such as these:

How did you start?

Did you use one silhouette at a time or did you try to put two or three silhouettes together at once?

What changes did you have to make as you worked?

How did you decide that you had the right building?

If students built only a $2 \times 2 \times 2$ cube, ask whether that is the only possible building to match the silhouettes.

Give students a minute or two to discuss this. If they seem unsure, remove any one cube from the $2 \times 2 \times 2$ cube and ask whether the building still matches the silhouettes. (It does.)

35 MIN INDIVIDUALS

ACTIVITY 3

Building from Silhouettes

Give students the remainder of the session to create buildings from silhouettes 2 and 3. Consider having additional small- or whole-group discussions.

Students will construct their buildings in various ways.

Encourage students to think of these buildings as a puzzle that may take some time to solve. It is unlikely that they will find answers quickly and easily. If students view the problems as challenging puzzles, they are more inclined to persevere in their search for answers.❷

ONGOING ASSESSMENT: Observing Students at Work

Using three silhouettes of a building, students build the structure with connecting cubes.

- **Are students able to make one building that can make all three silhouettes?**
- **How are students making the structure?** Are they building one silhouette first and then adding or subtracting cubes as they look at the other silhouettes?
- **Are they able to build by looking at more than one silhouette at a time (e.g., integrate two or three views and make the building without having to add or subtract cubes)?**

Professional Development

❷ **Teacher Note:** Integrating Three Views: How Students Try to Do It, p. 102

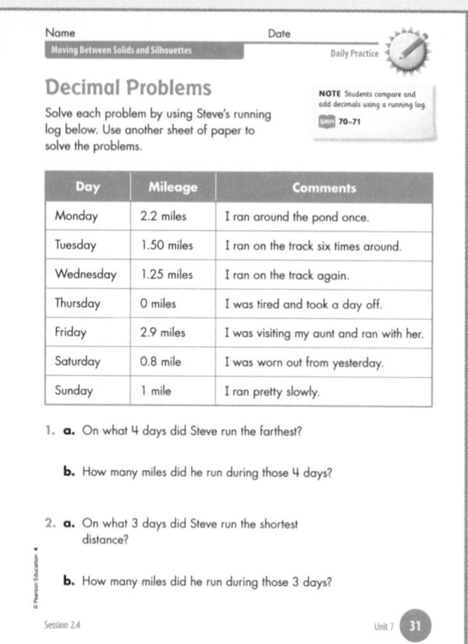
Name Date
Moving Between Solids and Silhouettes
Daily Practice

Decimal Problems

Solve each problem by using Steve's running log below. Use another sheet of paper to solve the problems.

NOTE Students compare and add decimals using a running log.
SMH 70–71

Day	Mileage	Comments
Monday	2.2 miles	I ran around the pond once.
Tuesday	1.50 miles	I ran on the track six times around.
Wednesday	1.25 miles	I ran on the track again.
Thursday	0 miles	I was tired and took a day off.
Friday	2.9 miles	I was visiting my aunt and ran with her.
Saturday	0.8 mile	I was worn out from yesterday.
Sunday	1 mile	I ran pretty slowly.

1. **a.** On what 4 days did Steve run the farthest?
   b. How many miles did he run during those 4 days?
2. **a.** On what 3 days did Steve run the shortest distance?
   b. How many miles did he run during those 3 days?

© Pearson Education 4
Session 2.4 Unit 7 31

▲ Student Activity Book, p. 31

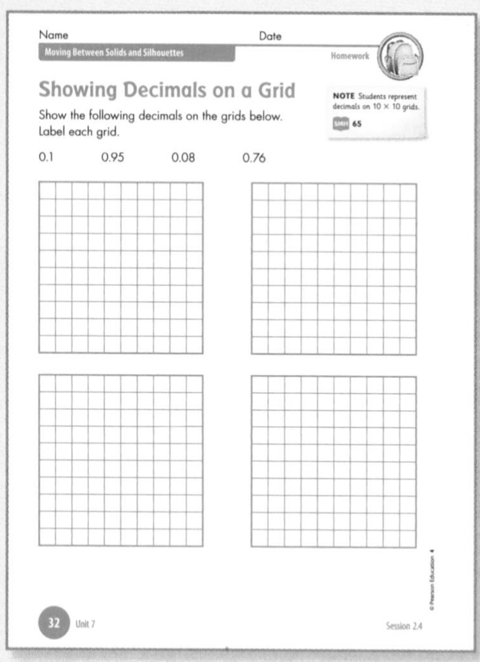
Name Date
Moving Between Solids and Silhouettes
Homework

Showing Decimals on a Grid

Show the following decimals on the grids below. Label each grid.

NOTE Students represent decimals on 10 × 10 grids.
SMH 65

0.1 0.95 0.08 0.76

© Pearson Education 4
32 Unit 7 Session 2.4

▲ Student Activity Book, p. 32

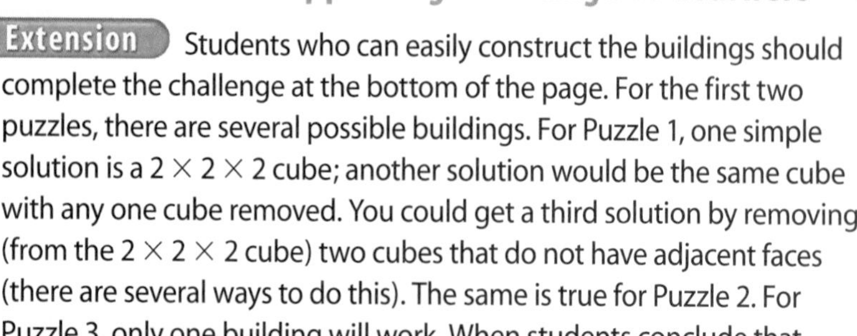
DIFFERENTIATION: Supporting the Range of Learners

Extension Students who can easily construct the buildings should complete the challenge at the bottom of the page. For the first two puzzles, there are several possible buildings. For Puzzle 1, one simple solution is a $2 \times 2 \times 2$ cube; another solution would be the same cube with any one cube removed. You could get a third solution by removing (from the $2 \times 2 \times 2$ cube) two cubes that do not have adjacent faces (there are several ways to do this). The same is true for Puzzle 2. For Puzzle 3, only one building will work. When students conclude that there is only one building for the third puzzle, ask them to explain why they are certain that there is only one building.

4 SESSION FOLLOW-UP

Daily Practice and Homework

Daily Practice: For ongoing review, have students complete *Student Activity Book* page 31.

Homework: Students represent decimals in the tenths and hundredths on a 10 × 10 grid on *Student Activity Book* page 32.

Student Math Handbook: Students and families may use *Student Math Handbook* page 124 for reference and review. See pages 119–121 in the back of this unit.

Assessment: Drawing Silhouettes

Math Focus Points

- Visualizing what 3-D figures look like from different perspectives
- Drawing silhouettes of 3-D cube buildings from different perspectives

Today's Plan		Materials
1 ACTIVITY **City Views**	25 MIN INDIVIDUALS	• *Student Activity Book*, p. 33 • Connecting cubes
2 DISCUSSION **Different Views**	15 MIN CLASS	• *Student Activity Book*, p. 33
3 ASSESSMENT ACTIVITY **Drawing Silhouettes**	20 MIN INDIVIDUALS	• M16–M17; M18
4 SESSION FOLLOW-UP **Daily Practice**		• *Student Activity Book*, p. 34 • *Student Math Handbook*, p. 124

Ten-Minute Math

Quick Images: 3-D Show Images 9 and 10 from *Quick Images: 3-D* (T75), and follow the procedure for the basic routine. For each image, have students discuss how they built their structures, including any revisions they made after each viewing. Ask questions such as these:

- How did you remember the parts of the image?
- What did you notice about the relationship of the parts of the image?
- What helped you remember the whole image, so that you could build your structure?

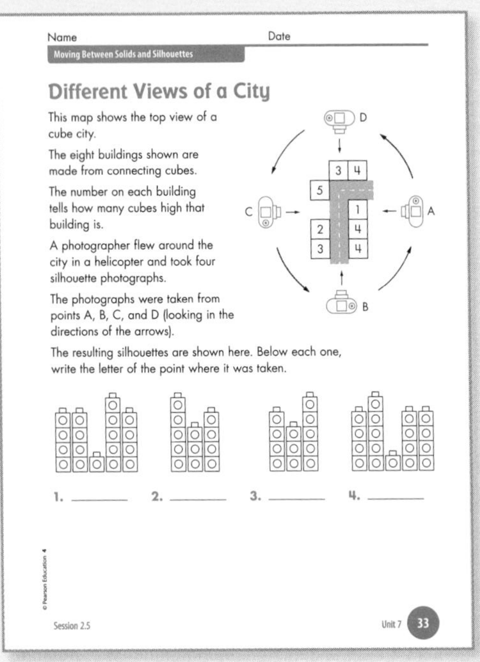

Name Date

Moving Between Solids and Silhouettes

Different Views of a City

This map shows the top view of a cube city.

The eight buildings shown are made from connecting cubes.

The number on each building tells how many cubes high that building is.

A photographer flew around the city in a helicopter and took four silhouette photographs.

The photographs were taken from points A, B, C, and D (looking in the directions of the arrows).

The resulting silhouettes are shown here. Below each one, write the letter of the point where it was taken.

1. ______ 2. ______ 3. ______ 4. ______

Session 2.5 Unit 7 33

▲ Student Activity Book, p. 33

ACTIVITY

1 City Views

25 MIN INDIVIDUALS

Direct students' attention to *Student Activity Book* page 33 and ask them to read the directions. Students first should try to match the silhouettes and the point from which each photograph was taken. Jot down their ideas above each of the silhouettes. Make sure that students understand that the number on each square represents how many cubes high a particular building is.

Students now build the cube city. When they have finished building, have them check with a neighbor or their small group to make sure that they all agree on what the cube city should look like. They write the letter of the point from where the picture was taken in the lines below the silhouettes.

Students should understand that the number on each square represents how many cubes high that building is.

ONGOING ASSESSMENT: Observing Students at Work

Students identify places on a "map" where different silhouettes can be seen.

- **Are students able to make a determination without building the city?** How close are their determinations?
- **Do students recognize cubes "in the back" or "on the other side of the street"?**

DIFFERENTIATION: Supporting the Range of Learners

Intervention Most students should be able to build the city of cubes. Have students who still need help in understanding perspective physically move around their cube city, crouching down and looking at each perspective. Remind them that it does not matter which building the cubes are on or the placement of the cube buildings; rather, they are looking for the highest tower of cubes from each perspective.

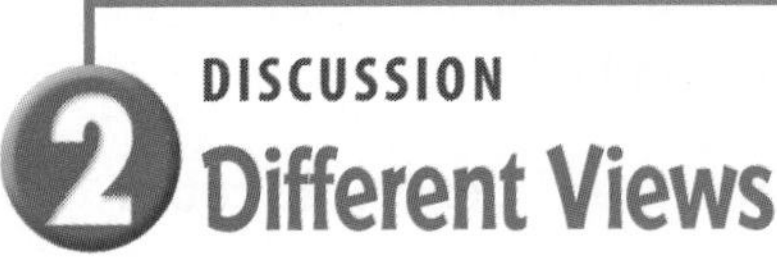

15 MIN CLASS

DISCUSSION

2 Different Views

Math Focus Points for Discussion

- Visualizing what 3-D figures look like from different perspectives

Discuss each silhouette on *Student Activity Book* page 33 and ask students what the correct answer is. (The correct answers are 1:A, 2:B, 3:D, 4:C.) Have students defend their answers, and have the class agree on the correct answers.

How close were you in your initial predictions? Which ones did you get correct? Which ones were not correct? How did making the actual cube buildings help you determine the correct answer?

20 MIN INDIVIDUALS

ASSESSMENT ACTIVITY

3 Drawing Silhouettes

Students choose from four images of cube buildings and draw the front, top, and right-side silhouettes of two of them on Assessment: Drawing Silhouettes (M16–M17). This assessment addresses Benchmark 2 of this unit.

- Draw 2-dimensional representations showing different perspectives of a 3-dimensional object.

Students who meet this benchmark:

- Use the same orientation for each building that they choose to draw silhouettes for;
- Correctly draw all three silhouettes for both buildings that they choose.

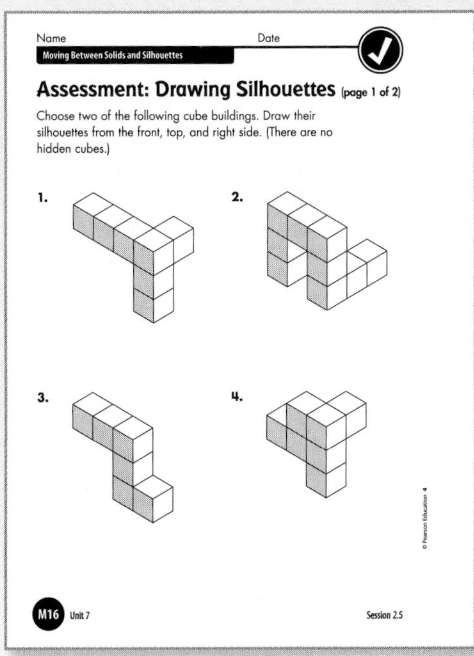

Name Date

Moving Between Solids and Silhouettes

Assessment: Drawing Silhouettes (page 1 of 2)

Choose two of the following cube buildings. Draw their silhouettes from the front, top, and right side. (There are no hidden cubes.)

1.

2.

3.

4.

M16 Unit 7 Session 2.5

▲ Resource Masters, M16 PORTFOLIO

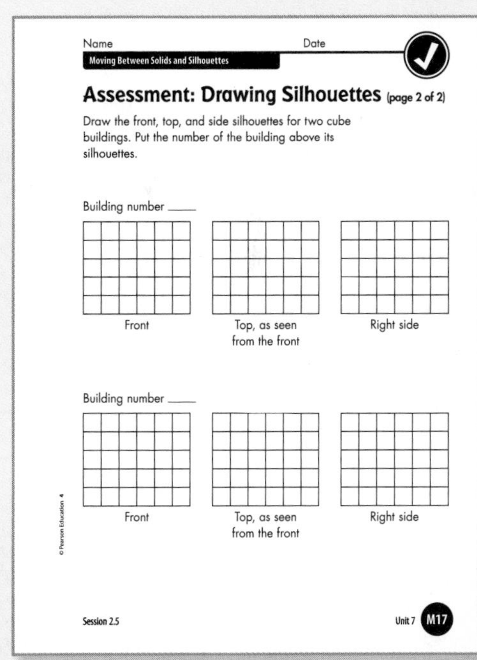

Name Date

Moving Between Solids and Silhouettes

Assessment: Drawing Silhouettes (page 2 of 2)

Draw the front, top, and side silhouettes for two cube buildings. Put the number of the building above its silhouettes.

Building number ____

Front | Top, as seen from the front | Right side

Building number ____

Front | Top, as seen from the front | Right side

Session 2.5 Unit 7 M17

▲ Resource Masters, M17 PORTFOLIO

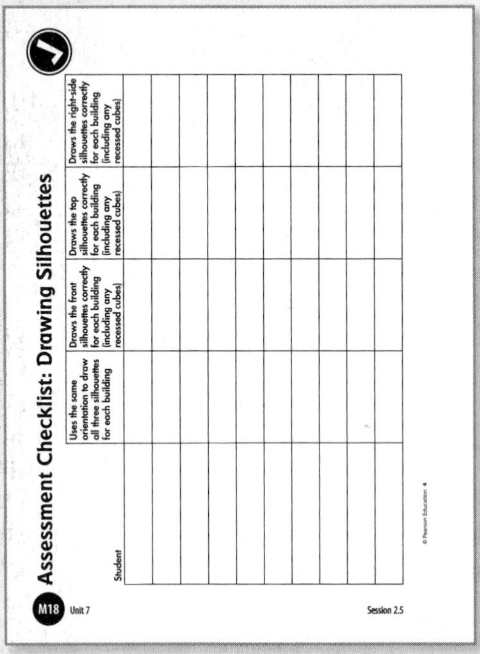

Assessment Checklist: Drawing Silhouettes

Student	Uses the same orientation to draw all three silhouettes for each building	Draws the front silhouettes correctly for each building (including any recessed cubes)	Draws the top silhouettes correctly for each building (including any recessed cubes)	Draws the right-side silhouettes correctly for each building (including any recessed cubes)

M18 Unit 7 Session 2.5

▲ Resource Masters, M18

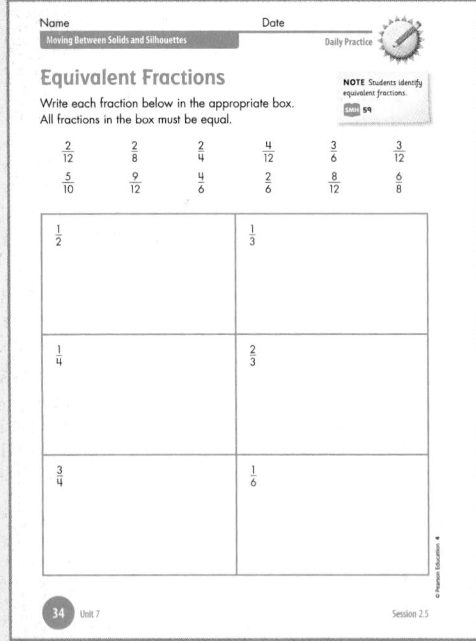

Name Date

Moving Between Solids and Silhouettes Daily Practice

Equivalent Fractions

NOTE Students identify equivalent fractions.

SMH 59

Write each fraction below in the appropriate box.
All fractions in the box must be equal.

$\frac{2}{12}$ $\frac{2}{8}$ $\frac{2}{4}$ $\frac{4}{12}$ $\frac{3}{6}$ $\frac{3}{12}$

$\frac{5}{10}$ $\frac{9}{12}$ $\frac{4}{6}$ $\frac{2}{6}$ $\frac{8}{12}$ $\frac{6}{8}$

$\frac{1}{2}$	$\frac{1}{3}$
$\frac{1}{4}$	$\frac{2}{3}$
$\frac{3}{4}$	$\frac{1}{6}$

34 Unit 7 Session 2.5

▲ Student Activity Book, p. 34

While students are working individually, use the Assessment Checklist: Drawing Silhouettes (M18) to help you assess students' ability to accurately visualize the 2-D silhouette that the building would project from each perspective. You may also use this checklist for your observations about students' work when you look at it later.

ONGOING ASSESSMENT: Observing Students at Work

Students draw front, top, and right-side silhouettes of cube buildings.

- **Do students draw all of the cubes for a given silhouette?** Are the cubes in the correct relationship to one another?
- **Are the students able to draw the "recessed" cubes (i.e., cubes that are not on the same plane)?**
- **Do students use the same orientation to draw each of the silhouettes?**

DIFFERENTIATION: Supporting the Range of Learners

Intervention At this point, it is likely that most students are able to draw the silhouettes without actually making the building; however, some may still need to build first. Students who need to build first in order to draw all of the silhouettes correctly still meet the benchmark. These students, as well as students who only partially meet the benchmark (e.g., they draw two of the three perspectives correctly for each building) and students who do not meet the benchmark, need more experience trying to draw the three views from images and checking their answers by building. The repeated comparisons of their images with the buildings will help students sharpen their visualization skills.

4 SESSION FOLLOW-UP
Daily Practice

Daily Practice: For ongoing review, have students complete *Student Activity Book* page 34.

Student Math Handbook: Students and families may use *Student Math Handbook* page 124 for reference and review. See pages 119–121 in the back of this unit.

INVESTIGATION 3

Mathematical Emphases

Features of Shape Translating between 2-dimensional and 3-dimensional shapes

Math Focus Points

- ◆ Drawing silhouettes of 3-D cube buildings from different perspectives

Volume Structuring rectangular prisms and determining their volume

Math Focus Points

- ◆ Seeing that cubes filling a rectangular prism can be decomposed into congruent layers
- ◆ Finding the volume of cube buildings
- ◆ Designing patterns for boxes that hold a given number of cubes (volume)
- ◆ Developing a strategy for determining the volume of rectangular prisms
- ◆ Finding the number of cubes (volume) that will fit into the box made by a given pattern
- ◆ Doubling the number of cubes for a given box and considering how that changes the dimensions of the original box

Understanding Volume

SESSION	Student Activity Book	Student Math Handbook	Professional Development: Read Ahead of Time
SESSION 3.1 p. 76 **How Many Cubes?** Students view pictures and patterns of rectangular boxes and determine how many unit cubes fit inside. They build the boxes and fill them with cubes to check their answer.	35–37	125–126	• **Teacher Note:** Strategies for Finding the Number of Cubes in 3-D Arrays, p. 103
SESSION 3.2 p. 81 **Patterns from the Bottom Up** Given the shape of the bottom of a box and its volume, students complete the design of the box.	39–44	125–126	
SESSION 3.3 p. 85 **Volume of Boxes** Students find the volume of rectangular prisms by drawing patterns and building boxes. They consider what happens when the volume of a given box is doubled. They write a general method for determining volume.	45–50	125–126	• **Dialogue Box:** Common Student Strategies for Doubling, p. 117
SESSION 3.4 p. 91 **Volume of Boxes, *continued*** Students continue to find the volume of rectangular prisms by drawing patterns and building boxes. They consider what happens when the volume of a given box is doubled. They refine their general method for determining volume.	46–48, 51	125–126	
SESSION 3.5 p. 94 **End-of-Unit Assessment** Students solve 3 problems to assess their understanding of volume and of translating between 3-dimensional and 2-dimensional representations of volume.	52	125–126	• **Teacher Note:** End-of-Unit Assessment, p. 106

Ten-Minute Math See page 16 for an overview.

Practicing Place Value

- **No materials needed**

Quick Images

- **T75–T76; *Quick Images: 3-D***
- **Connecting cubes (15–20 per student)**

Materials to Gather	Materials to Prepare
• **T78, The Packaging Factory** • **T79, How Many Cubes?** • **Connecting cubes** (70 per pair of students) • **Scissors** (1 per student) • **Transparent tape**	• **M21, Three-Quarter-Inch Grid Paper** Make copies. (2 per student plus at least 25 extra) • **Grid Paper** From three-quarter-inch grid paper, cut out the pattern for Box 1 on *Student Activity Book* page 35. Be ready to show students how to fold it together and tape it up to make a box. • **Connecting cubes** Create a rectangular prism with the dimensions $2 \times 3 \times 2$.
• **T81, Making Boxes from the Bottom Up** • **Scissors** (1 per student) • **Transparent tape** • **Erasable Marker**	• **M21, Three-Quarter-Inch Grid Paper** Make copies. (25 copies) (from Session 3.1).
• **T79, How Many Cubes?** • **Connecting cubes** (50 per student) • **Chart Paper** • **Erasable Marker**	• **M21, Three-Quarter-Inch Grid Paper** Make copies. (25 copies, plus 3 per student) • **Chart paper** Write the title "Strategies for Finding Volume."
• **Connecting cubes** (50 per student) • **Chart paper**	• **M21, Three-Quarter-Inch Grid Paper** Make copies. (25 copies, plus 3 per student) (from Session 3.1) • **Chart: "Strategies for Finding Volume"** (from Session 3.3)
	• **M23–M25, End-of-Unit Assessment** Make copies. (1 per student)

Overhead Transparency

How Many Cubes?

Math Focus Points

- Finding the number of cubes (volume) that will fit into the box made by a given pattern

Vocabulary

rectangular prism

Today's Plan			Materials
ACTIVITY 1 Introducing How Many Cubes?	10 MIN	CLASS	• T78 • grid paper*; rectangular prism made from connecting cubes*
ACTIVITY 2 How Many Cubes?	40 MIN	INDIVIDUALS	• *Student Activity Book,* p. 35 • M21*; T79 • Connecting cubes; scissors; transparent tape
DISCUSSION 3 Counting Cubes	10 MIN	CLASS	• *Student Activity Book,* p. 35
SESSION FOLLOW-UP 4 Daily Practice and Homework			• *Student Activity Book,* pp. 36–37 • *Student Math Handbook,* p. 63

*See *Materials to Prepare,* p. 75.

Ten-Minute Math

Practicing Place Value ***Write*** **26.3 on the board and have students practice** ***saying*** **it. Let students know that this number is commonly read both as "twenty-six and three tenths" and as "twenty-six point three." Make sure all students can read, write, and say this number correctly. Ask students to solve these problems mentally, if possible:**

- What is one tenth more than 26.3?
- What is 1 more?
- What is 10 more?

Write each answer on the board. Ask students to compare each sum with 26.3. Which places have the same digits? Which do not? Why? If time remains, pose additional similar questions using these numbers: 39.65 and 93.06.

ACTIVITY

Introducing How Many Cubes?

10 MIN CLASS

Display The Packaging Factory (T78) on the overhead projector. Cover the bottom half with a sheet of paper, revealing only the pictures of the single cube and the shipping boxes.①

Let's suppose that you are working at a packaging factory. Your company makes cardboard boxes of different shapes and sizes for packing and shipping products.

One product you package is a little ornament. Each ornament is the same size and is packaged in a little cube. [Point out the cube on the transparency.] You often need to ship more than one ornament at a time, so you pack the cubes in larger shipping boxes. [Point to larger boxes.] Over the next few days, we're going to work on determining how many cubes will fit in a shipping box and decide whether there's a way we can always accurately determine the number of cubes in a box.

Uncover the bottom half of the transparency and introduce the box-pattern diagrams.

To clarify the task, show the box pattern you have made from Three-Quarter-Inch Grid Paper (M21), demonstrating how the pattern shown on the transparency folds into a box. [Leave one side untaped, like an open top.] Hold up a single connecting cube, which students will use in this Investigation to represent one ornament.

Model for students how the box should be taped so that the sides do not overlap and the cubes fit in appropriately.

Math Note

① **Rectangular Prisms, Boxes, and 3-D Cube Arrays** A geometric solid is a shape that has 3 dimensions—length, width, and height. In mathematics, these shapes are called "solids" whether they are filled or hollow. A rectangular prism is a solid with 6 rectangular faces and edges that are perpendicular to one another. In this unit, students work with various representations of rectangular prisms, such as open boxes and congruent layers of cubes arranged in arrays. Each of these representations forms a solid in the shape of a rectangular prism.

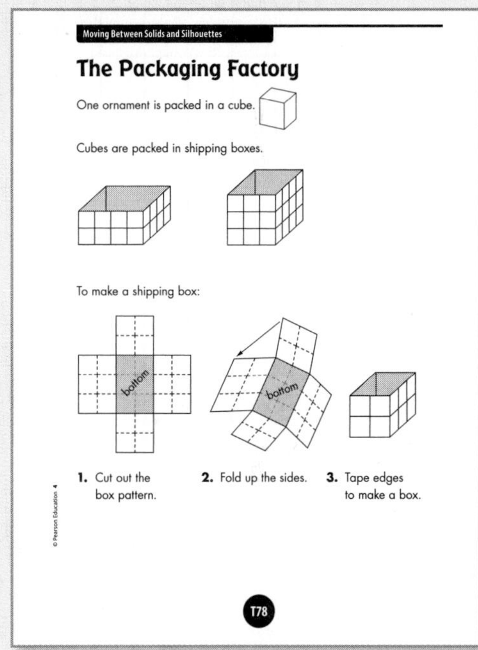

Moving Between Solids and Silhouettes

The Packaging Factory

One ornament is packed in a cube.

Cubes are packed in shipping boxes.

To make a shipping box:

1. Cut out the box pattern.
2. Fold up the sides.
3. Tape edges to make a box.

T78

▲ Transparencies, T78

Teaching Note

❷ **Finding Volume** Trying to determine volume before students use the cubes to find answers helps them form and organize mental images or models of the cube arrays. As students check their first answers, they refine these models and their ideas about figuring the number of cubes that will fit. Encourage students to think about discrepancies between their first answers and the actual count.

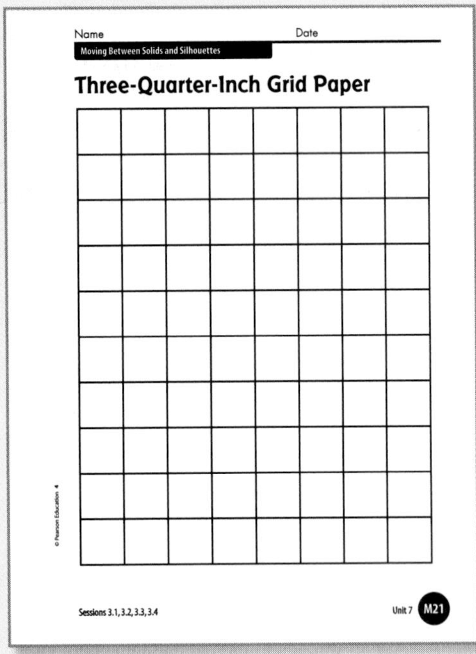
Name Date

Moving Between Solids and Silhouettes

Three-Quarter-Inch Grid Paper

Sessions 3.1, 3.2, 3.3, 3.4 Unit 7 M21

▲ Resource Masters, M21

Place the 2 × 3 × 2 rectangular prism you made inside the box to show how it fits. Point out to students that keeping one side of the box untaped makes it easier to place the cubes into the box and that they should do the same when making their patterns.

This demonstration is not intended to give students any suggestions of how to solve the problems in this activity. Therefore, do not discuss the number of cubes in your box or any methods for figuring the number of cubes at this time.

ACTIVITY

2 How Many Cubes?

40 MIN INDIVIDUALS

Display How Many Cubes? (T79), covering all but the pattern and picture for Box 1. Tell students to open up the *Student Activity Book* to page 35, which has the same exercise.

You're going to do some problems now to figure out the number of cubes that fit in a box. We'll use these cubes as the unit of measure to find the volume of the box. Here is a picture of a shipping box and a pattern that you could fold up to make the box.

Explain to students how to complete the assignment.

First, try to determine how many cubes will fit in the pictured box and write that number in the blank. Next, draw the box pattern on graph paper, cut it out, fold it, and tape the edges to make the box. Remember to leave one side untaped. Then, fill your box with cubes to check your first answer, and write down the actual number of cubes that fit in the box. Last, think about how close your first answer was to the actual count and why.

Tell students to complete all three boxes on page 35.❷

Encourage students who are successfully drawing a pattern to explain their strategy to other students. 3

ONGOING ASSESSMENT: Observing Students at Work

Students find the volume of given boxes.

- **How close are student predictions?** What strategies are they using to determine volume before they build?
- **Are students able to use the pattern to construct the box?** If not, what is confusing them?

DIFFERENTIATION: Supporting the Range of Learners

Intervention Students may not understand how the patterns fold into boxes, how parts of a pattern correspond to parts of a box, or how to draw the pictured pattern on graph paper. For students having difficulties, ask questions such as these:

- Is the pattern you've drawn on the graph paper exactly like the one pictured?
- Does each part of your pattern (bottom, sides) match the same parts in the pictured pattern?
- What part of the pattern will make this side of the box? [Indicate a side by pointing.]

Professional Development

3 **Teacher Note:** Strategies for Finding the Number of Cubes in 3-D Arrays, p. 103

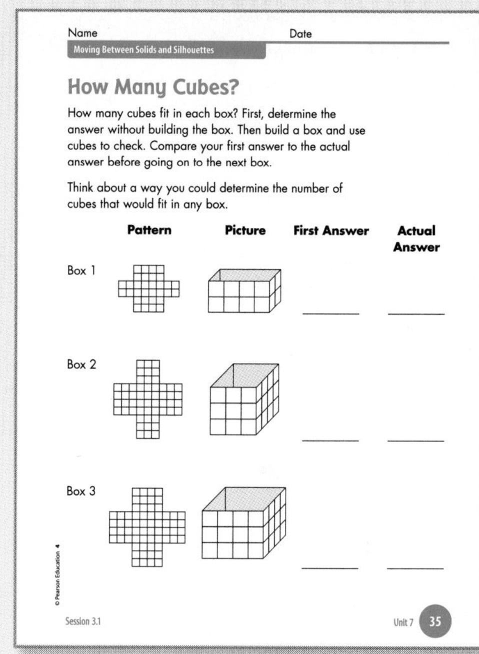

Name Date

Moving Between Solids and Silhouettes

How Many Cubes?

How many cubes fit in each box? First, determine the answer without building the box. Then build a box and use cubes to check. Compare your first answer to the actual answer before going on to the next box.

Think about a way you could determine the number of cubes that would fit in any box.

	Pattern	Picture	First Answer	Actual Answer
Box 1				
Box 2				
Box 3				

Session 3.1 Unit 7 35

▲ Student Activity Book, p. 35; Transparencies, T79

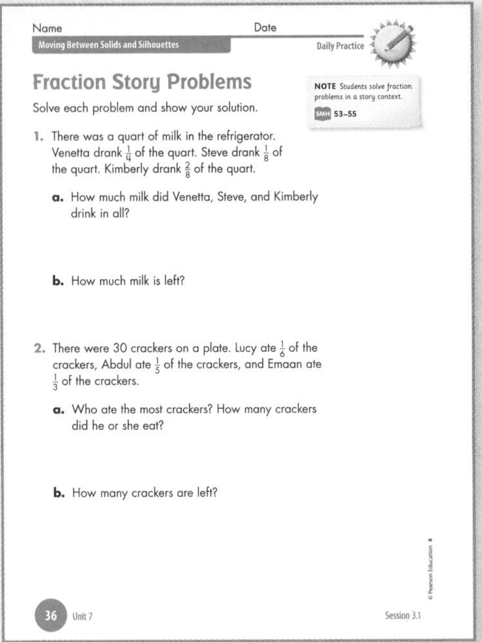

Name Date

Moving Between Solids and Silhouettes — Daily Practice

Fraction Story Problems

Solve each problem and show your solution.

NOTE Students solve fraction problems in a story context.

SMH 53–55

1. There was a quart of milk in the refrigerator. Venetta drank $\frac{1}{4}$ of the quart. Steve drank $\frac{1}{8}$ of the quart. Kimberly drank $\frac{2}{8}$ of the quart.
   a. How much milk did Venetta, Steve, and Kimberly drink in all?
   b. How much milk is left?
2. There were 30 crackers on a plate. Lucy ate $\frac{1}{6}$ of the crackers, Abdul ate $\frac{1}{5}$ of the crackers, and Emaan ate $\frac{1}{3}$ of the crackers.
   a. Who ate the most crackers? How many crackers did he or she eat?
   b. How many crackers are left?

36 Unit 7 Session 3.1

© Pearson Education 4

▲ Student Activity Book, p. 36

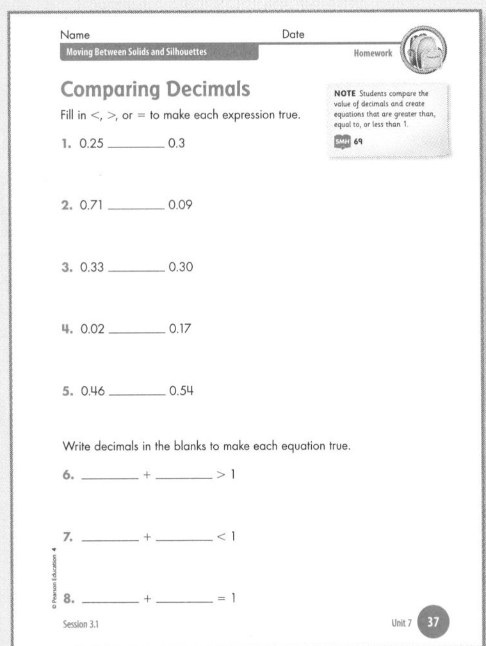

Name Date

Moving Between Solids and Silhouettes — Homework

Comparing Decimals

Fill in $<$, $>$, or $=$ to make each expression true.

NOTE Students compare the value of decimals and create equations that are greater than, equal to, or less than 1.

SMH 69

1. 0.25 ______ 0.3
2. 0.71 ______ 0.09
3. 0.33 ______ 0.30
4. 0.02 ______ 0.17
5. 0.46 ______ 0.54

Write decimals in the blanks to make each equation true.

6. ______ + ______ > 1
7. ______ + ______ < 1
8. ______ + ______ $= 1$

© Pearson Education 4

Session 3.1 Unit 7 37

▲ Student Activity Book, p. 37

10 MIN CLASS

3 DISCUSSION

Counting Cubes

Math Focus Points for Discussion

- Finding the number of cubes (volume) that will fit into the box made by a given pattern

After most students have completed *Student Activity Book* page 35, discuss how many cubes will fit in Box 2. Remind students that the best way to talk about the boxes and cubes is to both show and tell. If they use both the boxes and the cubes they made to fill the box, they will communicate more clearly. Ask questions such as these:

- How many cubes will fill Box 2? How did you count? Did anyone count a different way? How did the pattern help you count? How did looking at the box you made from the pattern help you count? How did the arrangement of the cubes help you count?

Expect students to count the number of cubes in a variety of ways.

Students might say:

"I made the box from the pattern. Then I filled it with cubes. I looked at the front of the box, and there are 9 cubes. Then I counted the rows and it's 4. So I did 9, 18, 27, and 36."

"My answer was 36 and I was right. There are 12 cubes that make the first layer in the box, that's the same number of squares for the bottom of the box. Then there are 3 layers. 12 × 3 is 36."

4 SESSION FOLLOW-UP

Daily Practice and Homework

Daily Practice: For ongoing review, have students complete *Student Activity Book* page 36.

Homework: Students compare decimals on *Student Activity Book* page 37.

Student Math Handbook: Students and families may use *Student Math Handbook* pages 125–126 for reference and review. See pages 119–121 in the back of this unit.

Patterns from the Bottom Up

Math Focus Points

- Designing patterns for boxes that hold a given number of cubes (volume)
- Seeing that cubes filling a rectangular prism can be decomposed into congruent layers

Today's Plan		Materials
DISCUSSION 1 **Patterns From the Bottom Up**	20 MIN INDIVIDUALS CLASS	• *Student Activity Book,* p. 39 • T81 • Scissors; transparent tape; erasable marker
ACTIVITY 2 **Designing Box Patterns**	40 MIN INDIVIDUALS	• *Student Activity Book,* pp. 40–42 • M21 (from Session 3.1)*
SESSION FOLLOW-UP 3 **Daily Practice and Homework**		• *Student Activity Book,* pp. 43–44 • *Student Math Handbook,* pp. 125–126

*See *Materials to Prepare,* p. 75.

Ten-Minute Math

Practicing Place Value **Say "eight hundred twelve and four tenths," and ask students to write the number. Make sure that all students can read, write, and say this number correctly. Ask students to solve these problems mentally, if possible:**

- What is 812.4 − 50?
- What is 812.4 + 50?
- What is 812.4 + 0.5?

Write each answer on the board.

Ask students to compare each sum and difference with 812.4. Which places have the same digits? Which do not? Why? If time remains, pose additional similar problems with the number: 40.51 and 77.03.

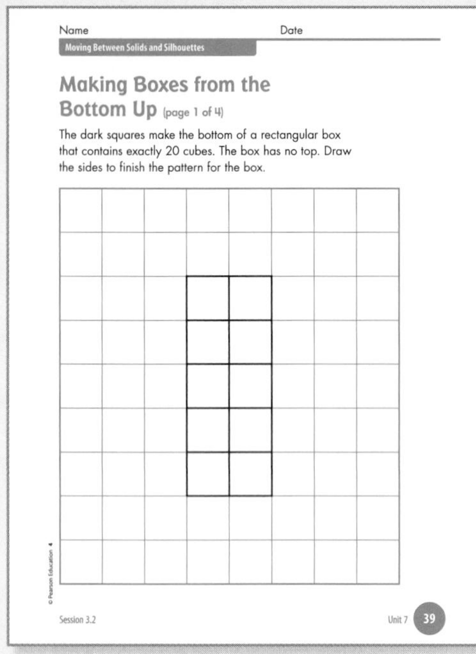
Name Date

Moving Between Solids and Silhouettes

Making Boxes from the Bottom Up (page 1 of 4)

The dark squares make the bottom of a rectangular box that contains exactly 20 cubes. The box has no top. Draw the sides to finish the pattern for the box.

© Pearson Education 4

Session 3.2 Unit 7 39

▲ Student Activity Book, p. 39; Transparencies, T81

DISCUSSION

Patterns From the Bottom Up

Math Focus Points

- Seeing that cubes filling a rectangular prism can be decomposed into congruent layers

Designing box patterns is a challenging task. Students develop strategies for designing patterns through repeated experiences, hearing and sharing ideas, and teacher guidance.

Display Making Boxes from the Bottom Up (T81) on the overhead projector and direct students' attention to the same grid on *Student Activity Book* page 39.

Yesterday, you used patterns to find out how many cube units a box would hold. Today, you're going to be given the bottom of the design, told the volume of the box, and asked to draw the design for the box. This is the bottom of a rectangular box that contains exactly 20 cubes. The box has no top. For now, draw the pattern for the box, but only the sides that come off the bottom.

After most students have had time to draw a pattern, ask them to discuss their strategies. Ask students to come to the overhead and use the transparency to show how they completed the pattern. Have them draw with an erasable marker. Ask questions such as these:

- How did you decide what the sides would look like? How many layers does your pattern have? How did you know how many layers there would be?

Allow students to show and discuss any patterns they designed, even if there is disagreement about what the pattern should be. After several students have explained their thinking, tell students to make the box from their pattern and test it by filling it with cubes.

After most students have finished making their pattern and filling it with cubes, ask whether their patterns were correct. Have them explain why they were or were not accurate.

Students' explanations will vary. Some students think that if the box holds 20 cubes, there must be 20 squares in the pattern. Other students know that there must be two layers of cubes, so that means two additional rows of squares on each "side" of the base. As students offer their explanations, make any revisions on the transparency that are necessary to get to the correct pattern.

ACTIVITY

Designing Box Patterns

40 MIN INDIVIDUALS

Students complete three more patterns on *Student Activity Book* pages 40–42. While students are working individually, use this as an opportunity to identify students who understand the activity and need to be challenged, as well as those who are struggling with the ideas and need additional help. Students get more experience with this type of problem in the Math Workshop in Sessions 3.3 and 3.4.

If students seem to be struggling with this work, have brief small- or whole-group discussions as needed.

ONGOING ASSESSMENT: Observing Students at Work

Students are shown the bottom of a box and design a pattern that will hold a given number of cubes.

- **What strategies are students using to complete the pattern?** Do they know how to draw the sides?
- **Are students able to figure out how many layers the box needs?** How do they figure it out? Do they use multiples and factors? Do they build the box, count, and make adjustments?
- **Do students understand the relationship between the actual box and the squares that appear on the pattern?** Do they understand which squares represent the "base" of the prism and which squares represent the "sides"?

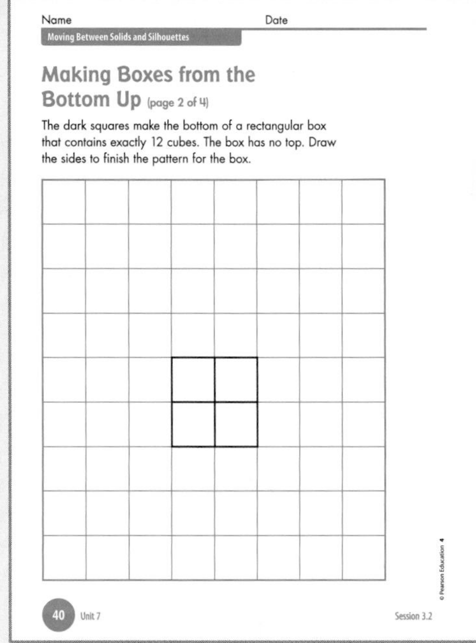

Name Date

Moving Between Solids and Silhouettes

Making Boxes from the Bottom Up (page 2 of 4)

The dark squares make the bottom of a rectangular box that contains exactly 12 cubes. The box has no top. Draw the sides to finish the pattern for the box.

40 Unit 7 Session 3.2

© Pearson Education 4

▲ Student Activity Book, p. 40

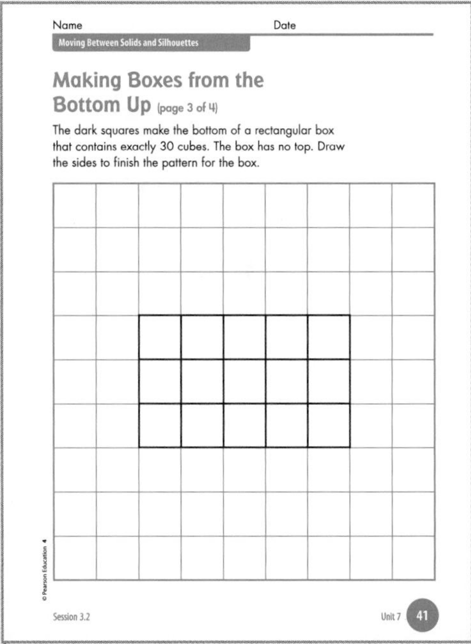

Name Date

Moving Between Solids and Silhouettes

Making Boxes from the Bottom Up (page 3 of 4)

The dark squares make the bottom of a rectangular box that contains exactly 30 cubes. The box has no top. Draw the sides to finish the pattern for the box.

Session 3.2 Unit 7 41

© Pearson Education 4

▲ Student Activity Book, pp. 41–42

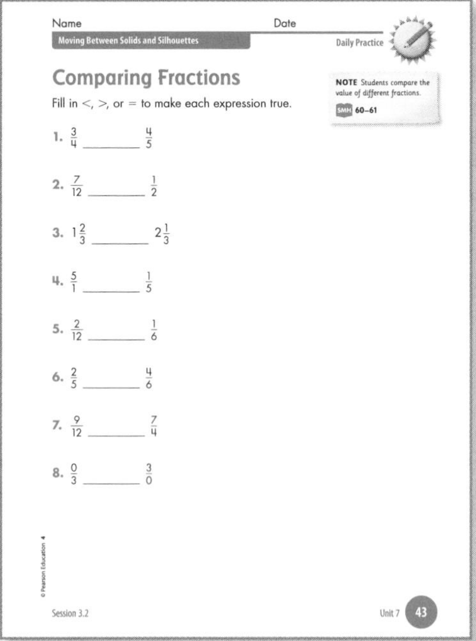
Name Date
Moving Between Solids and Silhouettes
Daily Practice

Comparing Fractions

Fill in $<$, $>$, or $=$ to make each expression true.

NOTE Students compare the value of different fractions.
SMH 60–61

1. $\frac{3}{4}$ ______ $\frac{4}{5}$
2. $\frac{7}{12}$ ______ $\frac{1}{2}$
3. $1\frac{2}{3}$ ______ $2\frac{1}{3}$
4. $\frac{5}{1}$ ______ $\frac{1}{5}$
5. $\frac{2}{12}$ ______ $\frac{1}{6}$
6. $\frac{2}{5}$ ______ $\frac{4}{6}$
7. $\frac{9}{12}$ ______ $\frac{7}{4}$
8. $\frac{0}{3}$ ______ $\frac{3}{0}$

© Pearson Education 4

Session 3.2 Unit 7 43

▲ Student Activity Book, p. 43

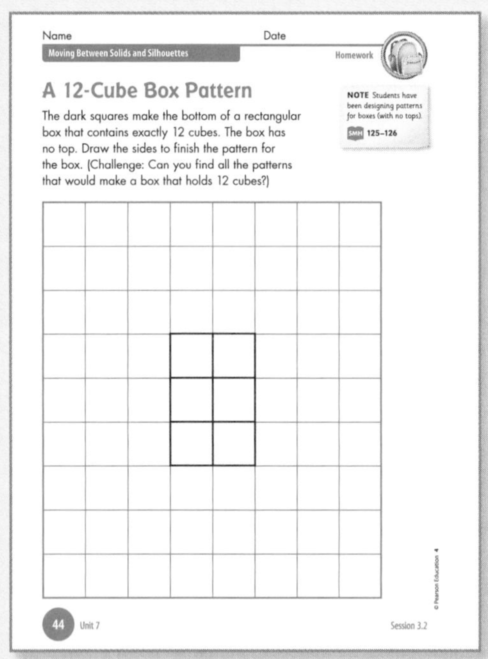
Name Date
Moving Between Solids and Silhouettes
Homework

A 12-Cube Box Pattern

The dark squares make the bottom of a rectangular box that contains exactly 12 cubes. The box has no top. Draw the sides to finish the pattern for the box. (Challenge: Can you find all the patterns that would make a box that holds 12 cubes?)

NOTE Students have been designing patterns for boxes (with no tops).
SMH 125–126

© Pearson Education 4

44 Unit 7 Session 3.2

▲ Student Activity Book, p. 44

DIFFERENTIATION: Supporting the Range of Learners

Intervention To make the patterns, or even to understand them, some students will need to make the cube configurations that fit in the boxes first, place them on the patterns, and figure out what the sides would look like. If they are still not sure how to proceed, ask them questions such as these:

- **How tall is the box?**
- **How many layers does it have?**
- **How many rows of squares do you need on each side to show how many layers the box has?**

SESSION FOLLOW-UP

3 Daily Practice and Homework

Daily Practice: For ongoing review, have students complete *Student Activity Book* page 43.

Homework: Students complete a design to build a 12-cube box and are challenged to find all possible boxes for 12 cubes on *Student Activity Book* page 44.

Student Math Handbook: Students and families may use *Student Math Handbook* pages 125–126 for reference and review. See pages 119–121 in the back of this unit.

SESSION 3.3

Volume of Boxes

Math Focus Points

- Seeing that cubes filling a rectangular prism can be decomposed into congruent layers
- Developing a strategy for determining the volume of rectangular prisms
- Doubling the number of cubes for a given box and considering how that changes the dimensions of the original box

Today's Plan		Materials
1 MATH WORKSHOP **Finding Volume** 1A Finding the Volume of More Boxes 1B Building Boxes from the Bottom Up 1C Double the Number of Cubes	45 MIN	1A • *Student Activity Book,* pp. 45, 46, 48 • M21*; T79 • Connecting cubes; erasable marker 1B • *Student Activity Book,* p. 46 • M21* • Connecting cubes 1C • *Student Activity Book,* p. 47 • Connecting cubes
2 DISCUSSION **Strategies for Finding Volume**	15 MIN CLASS	• *Student Activity Book,* p. 48 • Chart: "Strategies for Finding Volume"
3 SESSION FOLLOW-UP **Daily Practice and Homework**		• *Student Activity Book,* pp. 49–50 • *Student Math Handbook,* pp. 125–126

*See *Materials to Prepare,* p. 75.

Ten-Minute Math

Quick Images: 3-D **Show Images 11 and 12 from *Quick Images: 3-D* (T75), and follow the procedure for the basic routine. For each image, students discuss how they built their structures, including any revisions they made after each viewing. Ask:**

- How did you remember the parts of the image?
- What did you notice about the relationship of the parts of the image?
- What helped you remember the whole image, so that you could build your structure?

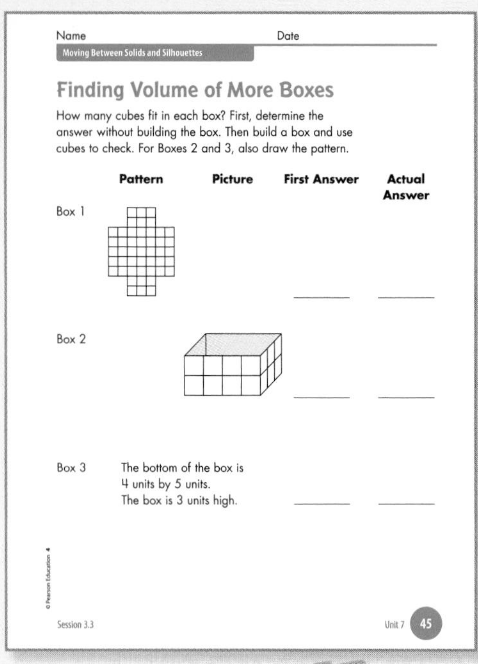

Name Date

Moving Between Solids and Silhouettes

Finding Volume of More Boxes

How many cubes fit in each box? First, determine the answer without building the box. Then build a box and use cubes to check. For Boxes 2 and 3, also draw the pattern.

	Pattern	Picture	First Answer	Actual Answer
Box 1			____	____
Box 2			____	____
Box 3	The bottom of the box is 4 units by 5 units. The box is 3 units high.		____	____

© Pearson Education 4

Session 3.3 Unit 7 45

▲ Student Activity Book, p. 45 PORTFOLIO

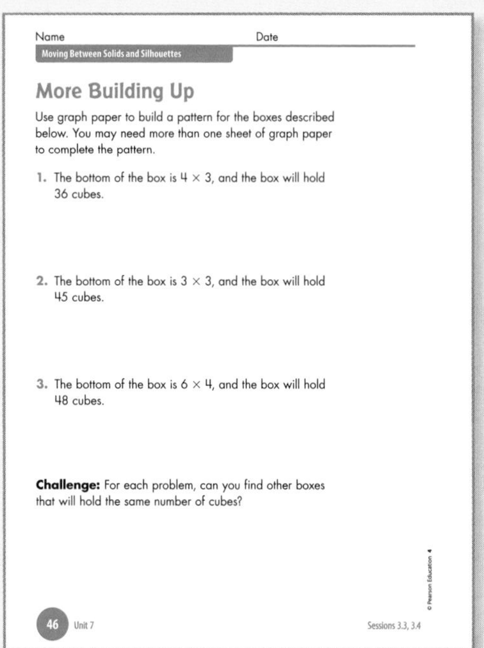

Name Date

Moving Between Solids and Silhouettes

More Building Up

Use graph paper to build a pattern for the boxes described below. You may need more than one sheet of graph paper to complete the pattern.

1. The bottom of the box is 4×3, and the box will hold 36 cubes.
2. The bottom of the box is 3×3, and the box will hold 45 cubes.
3. The bottom of the box is 6×4, and the box will hold 48 cubes.

Challenge: For each problem, can you find other boxes that will hold the same number of cubes?

© Pearson Education 4

46 Unit 7 Sessions 3.3, 3.4

▲ Student Activity Book, p. 46

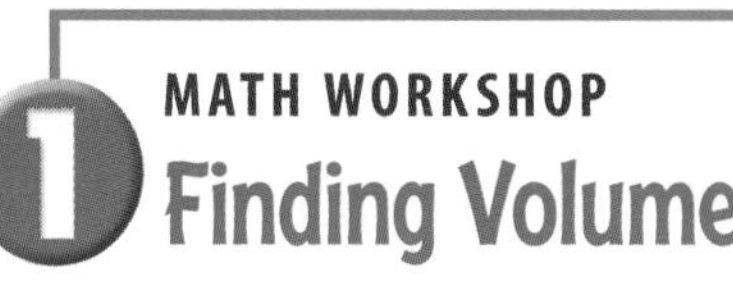

MATH WORKSHOP

1 Finding Volume

45 MIN

Students will continue with these Math Workshop activities in Session 3.4. They have already done two of the activities; the third is new. As they work on the activities today, students also work on *Student Activity Book* page 45. The discussion at the end of this session focuses on different ways to find volume.

Before beginning the Math Workshop, briefly explain to students how dimensions can be used to describe the rectangular prisms they have built.

Remind students how they labeled the dimensions of the arrays they used earlier in the year. Tell them that similar notation can be used to describe the dimensions of 3-dimensional objects.

Display Box 1, a rectangular prism, on How Many Cubes? (T79).

If we wanted to describe the dimensions of this prism, what 3 numbers would we use? (2, 4, 2)

Remind students that dimensions can be written with an "×," which reads as "by" and not "times." With an erasable marker, write the dimensions as $2 \times 4 \times 2$ on the transparency, under the picture box.

For the purposes of the activities you'll be doing, the order of the numbers isn't really important. What is important is that you know what each of the numbers represents. [As you say the number of each dimension, point to that dimension on Box 1.] Some of you may say that the prism is $4 \times 2 \times 2$, others may say $2 \times 2 \times 4$, and others might even describe the prism by saying that it is 4×2 on the bottom and 2 high. You will use dimensions to describe prisms in the new activity of the Math Workshop, Double the Number of Cubes.

1A Finding the Volume of More Boxes

INDIVIDUALS

On *Student Activity Book* page 46, students find the volume of rectangular prisms by using either a pattern or the dimensions. This is a continuation of the work in Session 3.1. But here students also complete *Student Activity Book* page 48 and write about several ways they could find the volume of any rectangular prism.

ONGOING ASSESSMENT: Observing Students at Work

Students find the volume of boxes by looking at drawings or a description and then check their answers by building the boxes.

- **Are students able to find the volume without building the box?** What strategies are they using to determine volume?
- **Are students able to use the pattern alone to construct the box?** If not, what is confusing them?
- **Are students able to make the pattern for Boxes 2 and 3?**

DIFFERENTIATION: Supporting the Range of Learners

Intervention Students who are still working on translating between the 2-D representation and the 3-D building should spend a majority of their Math Workshop time on this activity. Students who can do this work easily should spend more time on the doubling activity.

1B Building Boxes from the Bottom Up

INDIVIDUALS

Using Three-Quarter-Inch Grid Paper (M21) and the prompts on *Student Activity Book* page 46, students build a set of open boxes when given the dimensions of the bottom of each box and the total number of cubes in the box.

ONGOING ASSESSMENT: Observing Students at Work

Students build boxes when given the dimensions of the bottom and the total number of cubes.

- **What strategies are students using to make the pattern?** Do they know how to draw the bottom? The sides?
- **Do students understand how many "layers" of cubes they need for the given number of cubes?** How do they figure that out?
- **Do students see the relationship between the number of layers and the number of squares they need to draw for each side?**

DIFFERENTIATION: Supporting the Range of Learners

Intervention Students who are still developing spatial relationships will benefit from spending more time on this activity. You may need to make up additional problems.

Extension Students who can easily complete these boxes can be challenged to find all of the possible boxes for the given number of cubes. (For example, Box 1 has 36 cubes, and the bottom is 4 × 3; ask students to find the other boxes that hold 36 cubes, regardless of the sizes of the bottoms.)

1C Double the Number of Cubes

INDIVIDUALS

On *Student Activity Book* page 47, students are given the dimensions of a box and asked to find boxes that will hold twice as many cubes.① ② All students should try this activity because it will be part of the discussion on the second day of the Math Workshop. If you find that students are confused by the directions, briefly go over the directions with the whole class and make sure that students understand the task.③

ONGOING ASSESSMENT: Observing Students at Work

Students explore the relationship between the dimensions of a box and doubling the number of cubes in the box.

- **Do students understand the relationship between changing the dimensions of a box and how many cubes will fit in the box?**
- **How do students solve this problem?** Do they double the number of cubes (in this case from 24 to 48) and then figure out what the dimensions could be, or do they double one or more of the dimensions to see how many cubes would be needed?

DIFFERENTIATION: Supporting the Range of Learners

Intervention Students who are still developing spatial relationships should do this activity, but they should spend more time on the other two activities.

Extension Students who have a stronger understanding should be encouraged to find all the boxes that would hold twice (or half) as many cubes and explore the relationships of those dimensions. (All possibilities will be factors of the total number of cubes.)

Math Note

① **Doubling the Number of Cubes** The goal of this activity is for students to see the connection between changing the dimensions of a box and changing the number of cubes that fit in the box. One way to double the number of cubes is to double *one* of the original dimensions. There are also other ways. Some students might explain that they simply looked for sets of 3 numbers that multiply together to get 48; others explain that they started with a layer of 6 and then determined how many layers they needed to have 48 cubes.

Differentiation

② **English Language Learners** English Language Learners must understand the expressions *double* and *twice as many as* in order to participate in this activity. To help English Language Learners comprehend these expressions, you can demonstrate them one-on-one or with a small group. Take three objects, such as pencils, and ask students to count how many there are. Now tell them you want to double that amount. Add the appropriate amount to the collection. How many pencils do I have now? Yes, six is *twice as many as* three. Next ask students to double it again. Now I want you to *double* this amount of pencils. How many pencils are there now? Yes, now there are twelve. Twelve is *twice as many as* six. Continue doubling the pencils, or ask students to repeat the process using other objects. You can follow with a discussion of multiplying by two in order to double an amount.

Professional Development

③ **Dialogue Box:** Common Student Strategies for Doubling, p. 117

DISCUSSION

Strategies for Finding Volume

Math Focus Points for Discussion

- Developing a strategy for determining the volume of rectangular prisms

Give students about 5 minutes to discuss with a partner, or in a small group, their answers on *Student Activity Book* page 48.

Post the chart paper titled "Strategies for Finding Volume." Call students together and have a whole-class discussion about what strategies students are using to find the total number of cubes.

As students explain their thinking, write their strategies on the chart. Have students ask questions of one another and defend and clarify their thinking.

Students might say:

"I look to see how many cubes are on the face facing me. I count them and then I multiply that number by how long the box is." (This student is multiplying the number of cubes in a vertical layer by the number of vertical layers.)

"The top face is one number times another number—however many cubes there are on each side of the top—you know, the dimensions. Then it's multiplied by however many layers there are."

"Count the dimensions, each direction, and multiply them. Or you can count how many cubes are on one layer and then multiply that number by the number of layers there are."

Tell students that in the next session, they will have more time to work on, and further discuss, their strategies.

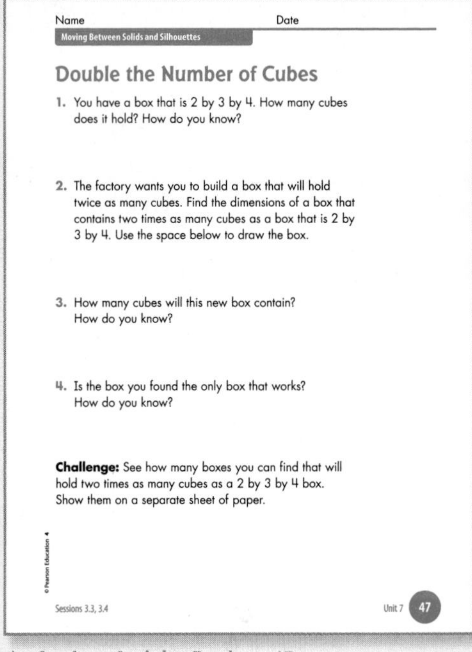
Name Date
Moving Between Solids and Silhouettes

Double the Number of Cubes

1. You have a box that is 2 by 3 by 4. How many cubes does it hold? How do you know?

2. The factory wants you to build a box that will hold twice as many cubes. Find the dimensions of a box that contains two times as many cubes as a box that is 2 by 3 by 4. Use the space below to draw the box.

3. How many cubes will this new box contain? How do you know?

4. Is the box you found the only box that works? How do you know?

Challenge: See how many boxes you can find that will hold two times as many cubes as a 2 by 3 by 4 box. Show them on a separate sheet of paper.

© Pearson Education 4

Sessions 3.3, 3.4 Unit 7 47

▲ Student Activity Book, p. 47

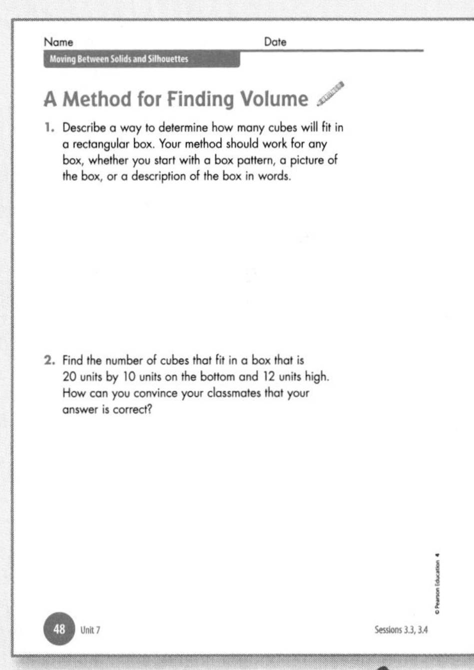
Name Date
Moving Between Solids and Silhouettes

A Method for Finding Volume

1. Describe a way to determine how many cubes will fit in a rectangular box. Your method should work for any box, whether you start with a box pattern, a picture of the box, or a description of the box in words.

2. Find the number of cubes that fit in a box that is 20 units by 10 units on the bottom and 12 units high. How can you convince your classmates that your answer is correct?

© Pearson Education 4

48 Unit 7 Sessions 3.3, 3.4

▲ Student Activity Book, p. 48

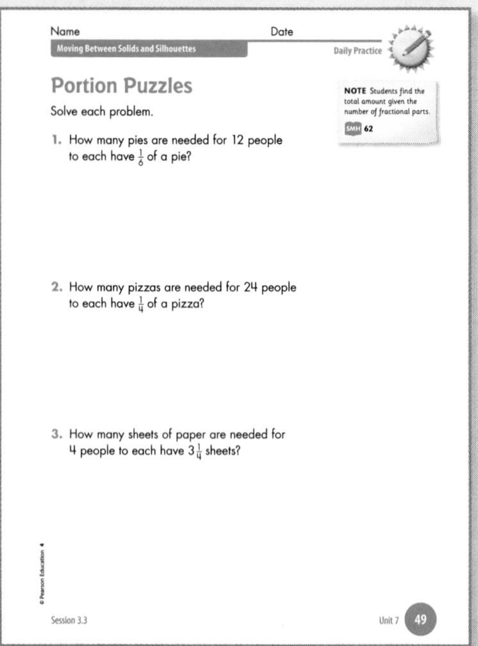

Name Date

Moving Between Solids and Silhouettes

Daily Practice

Portion Puzzles

Solve each problem.

NOTE Students find the total amount given the number of fractional parts.

SMH 62

1. How many pies are needed for 12 people to each have $\frac{1}{6}$ of a pie?

2. How many pizzas are needed for 24 people to each have $\frac{1}{4}$ of a pizza?

3. How many sheets of paper are needed for 4 people to each have $3\frac{1}{4}$ sheets?

© Pearson Education 4

Session 3.3 Unit 7 49

▲ Student Activity Book, p. 49

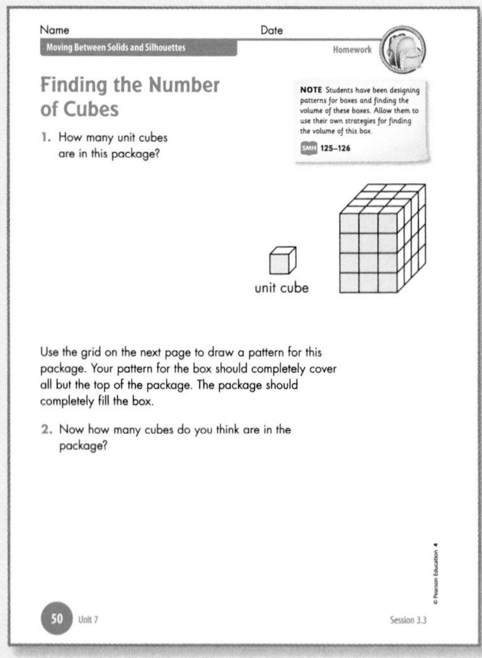

Name Date

Moving Between Solids and Silhouettes

Homework

Finding the Number of Cubes

NOTE Students have been designing patterns for boxes and finding the volume of these boxes. Allow them to use their own strategies for finding the volume of this box.

SMH 125–126

1. How many unit cubes are in this package?

unit cube

Use the grid on the next page to draw a pattern for this package. Your pattern for the box should completely cover all but the top of the package. The package should completely fill the box.

2. Now how many cubes do you think are in the package?

© Pearson Education 4

50 Unit 7 Session 3.3

▲ Student Activity Book, p. 50

3 SESSION FOLLOW-UP

Daily Practice and Homework

Daily Practice: For ongoing review, have students complete *Student Activity Book* page 49.

Homework: Students look at a diagram of a box and find its volume on *Student Activity Book* page 50.

Student Math Handbook: Students and families may use *Student Math Handbook* pages 125–126 for reference and review. See pages 119–121 in the back of this unit.

Volume of Boxes, *continued*

Math Focus Points

- Seeing that cubes filling a rectangular prism can be decomposed into congruent layers
- Developing a strategy for determining the volume of rectangular prisms
- Doubling the number of cubes for a given box and considering how that changes the dimensions of the original box

Today's Plan		Materials
1 MATH WORKSHOP **Finding Volume,** *continued* 1A Finding the Volume of More Boxes 1B Building Boxes from the Bottom Up 1C Double the Number of Cubes	45 MIN	1A • *Student Activity Book,* pp. 46, 48 • M21* • Connecting cubes 1B • *Student Activity Book,* p. 46 • M21* • Connecting cubes 1C • *Student Activity Book,* p. 47 • Connecting cubes
2 DISCUSSION **Strategies for Finding Volume,** *continued*	15 MIN CLASS	• *Student Activity Book,* pp. 47–48 • Chart: "Strategies for Finding Volume" (from Session 3.3)
3 SESSION FOLLOW-UP **Daily Practice**		• *Student Activity Book,* p. 51 • *Student Math Handbook,* pp. 125–126

*See *Materials to Prepare,* p. 75.

Ten-Minute Math

Quick Images: 3-D **Show Images 13 and 14 from *Quick Images:* 3-D (T76), and follow the procedure for the basic routine. For each image, students discuss how they built their structures, including any revisions they made after each viewing. Ask:**

- How did you remember the parts of the image?
- What did you notice about the relationship of the parts of the image?
- What helped you remember the whole image so that you could build your structure?

Moving Between Solids and Silhouettes

Quick Images: 3-D (page 3 of 3)

13.	14.
15.	16.

T76

▲ Transparencies, T76

45 MIN

MATH WORKSHOP
Finding Volume, *continued*

Students complete three activities in this second day of a Math Workshop. They continue to think about general methods for finding volume. They also add to or revise their work on *Student Activity Book* page 48. The discussion at the end of this session focuses on this general method, as well as consideration of the effect of doubling the number of cubes.

Students continue to learn about the relationship between the number of layers and the number of squares that they need to draw for each side.

1A Finding the Volume of More Boxes

INDIVIDUALS

See Session 3.3 page 86 for a full description of this activity.

1B Building Boxes from the Bottom Up

INDIVIDUALS

See Session 3.3 page 87 for a full description of this activity.

1C Double the Number of Cubes

INDIVIDUALS

See Session 3.3 page 88 for a full description of this activity.

DISCUSSION

2 Strategies for Finding Volume, *continued*

Math Focus Points for Discussion

- Developing a strategy for determining the volume of rectangular prisms
- Doubling the number of cubes for a given box and considering how that changes the dimensions of the original box

Draw students' attention to the chart the class created yesterday, "Strategies for Finding Volume." Have another discussion about general methods students are devising to find the number of cubes in a box. Most students are expected to have at least one strategy that they can use to find the volume of a rectangular prism. On the basis of students' writing on *Student Activity Book* page 48, ask:

- As you worked today, did anyone have new ideas or things to add to our discussion from yesterday?

Next, ask students what they have discovered about doubling the number of cubes.

Look at *Student Activity Book* page 47. What are the dimensions of the boxes you found that will hold twice as many cubes? [List these where everyone can see them.] What do you notice about these dimensions? How did you find the dimensions of boxes that contain twice as many cubes as the original box? Did anyone start by doubling all of the dimensions? What did you find?

Students should notice that to double the number of cubes in a prism, only one dimension is doubled. If two of the dimensions are doubled, the volume is increased 4 times; if all of the dimensions are doubled, the volume is increased 8 times.

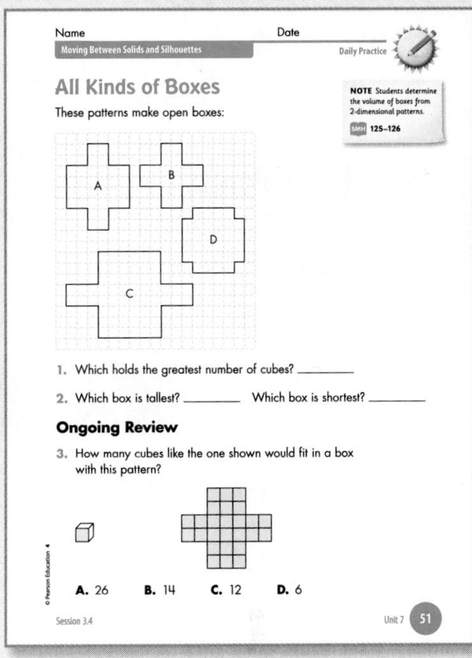

Name Date

Moving Between Solids and Silhouettes — Daily Practice

All Kinds of Boxes

These patterns make open boxes:

NOTE Students determine the volume of boxes from 2-dimensional patterns. SMH 125–126

1. Which holds the greatest number of cubes? ______
2. Which box is tallest? ______ Which box is shortest? ______

Ongoing Review

3. How many cubes like the one shown would fit in a box with this pattern?

A. 26 **B.** 14 **C.** 12 **D.** 6

Session 3.4 Unit 7 51

▲ Student Activity Book, p. 51

SESSION FOLLOW-UP

3 Daily Practice

Daily Practice: For reinforcement of this unit's content, have students complete *Student Activity Book* page 51.

Student Math Handbook: Students and families may use *Student Math Handbook* pages 125–126 for reference and review. See pages 119–121 in the back of this unit.

End-of-Unit Assessment

Math Focus Points

- Drawing silhouettes of 3-D cube buildings from different perspectives
- Finding the volume of cube buildings

Today's Plan	Materials
1 ASSESSMENT ACTIVITY **End-of-Unit Assessment** 60 MIN INDIVIDUALS	• M23–M25*
2 SESSION FOLLOW-UP **Daily Practice**	• *Student Activity Book,* p. 52 • *Student Math Handbook,* pp. 125–126

*See *Materials to Prepare,* p. 75.

Ten-Minute Math

Quick Images: 3-D **Show Images 15 and 16 from *Quick Images: 3-D* (T76) and follow the procedure for the basic routine. For each image, students discuss how they built their structures, including any revisions they made after each viewing. Ask questions such as these:**

- How did you remember the parts of the image?
- What did you notice about the relationship of the parts of the image?
- What helped you remember the whole image so that you could build your structure?

1 ASSESSMENT ACTIVITY
End-of-Unit Assessment

This assessment consists of three problems on End-of-Unit Assessment (M23–M25). In the first problem, students are asked to make a cube building and show it to you before they draw its silhouettes.[1] This exercise addresses Benckmark 2: Draw 2-dimensional representations showing different perspectives of a 3-dimensional object. Check each student's structure to make sure that it is correct. The other two problems deal with ideas of volume and address Benchmark 3: Find the volume of cube buildings and rectangular prisms.

It is unlikely that all students will need the entire 60 minutes to complete this assessment. Consider having students complete Math Workshop activities from Sessions 3.3 and 3.4. After all students have finished the assessment, have a class discussion about solutions to the assessment problems.

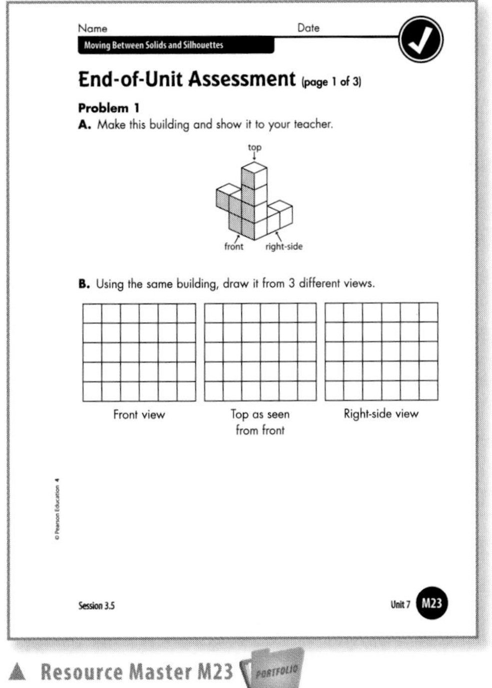

Name Date

Moving Between Solids and Silhouettes

End-of-Unit Assessment (page 1 of 3)

Problem 1

A. Make this building and show it to your teacher.

B. Using the same building, draw it from 3 different views.

Session 3.5 Unit 7 M23

▲ Resource Master M23 PORTFOLIO

Professional Development

[1] **Teacher Note:** End-of-Unit Assessment, p. 106

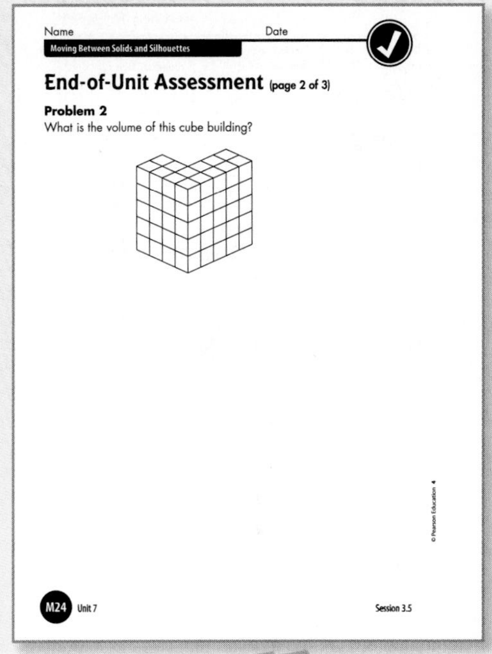

Name Date

Moving Between Solids and Silhouettes

End-of-Unit Assessment (page 2 of 3)

Problem 2

What is the volume of this cube building?

M24 Unit 7 Session 3.5

▲ Resource Master M24 PORTFOLIO

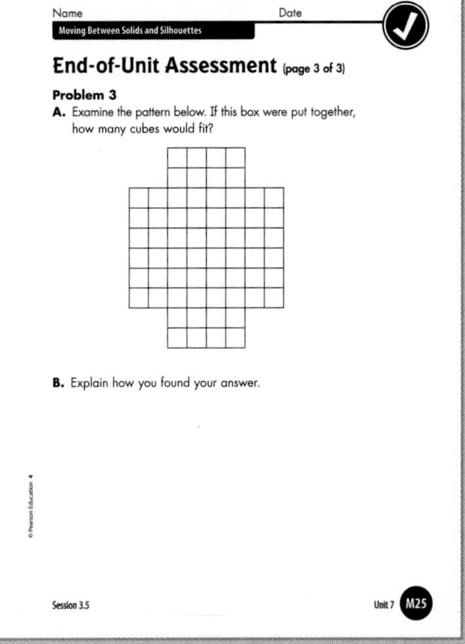

Name Date

Moving Between Solids and Silhouettes

End-of-Unit Assessment (page 3 of 3)

Problem 3

A. Examine the pattern below. If this box were put together, how many cubes would fit?

B. Explain how you found your answer.

Session 3.5 Unit 7 M25

▲ Resource Master M25

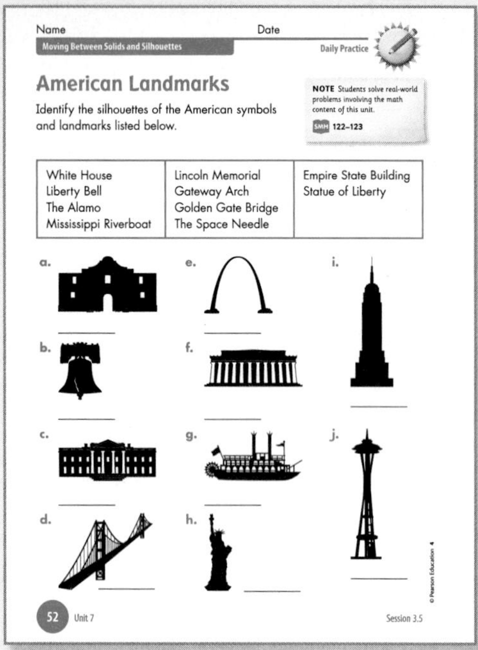
Name Date

Moving Between Solids and Silhouettes

Daily Practice

American Landmarks

Identify the silhouettes of the American symbols and landmarks listed below.

NOTE Students solve real-world problems involving the math content of this unit.

SMH 122–123

White House Liberty Bell The Alamo Mississippi Riverboat	Lincoln Memorial Gateway Arch Golden Gate Bridge The Space Needle	Empire State Building Statue of Liberty

a. ______ e. ______ i. ______

b. ______ f. ______

c. ______ g. ______ j. ______

d. ______ h. ______

© Pearson Education 4

52 Unit 7 Session 3.5

▲ Student Activity Book, p. 52

2 SESSION FOLLOW-UP
Daily Practice

Daily Practice: For enrichment, have students complete *Student Activity Book* page 52.

Student Math Handbook: Students and families may use *Student Math Handbook* pages 125–126 for reference and review. See pages 119–121 in the back of this unit.

Professional Development

UNIT 7

Moving Between Solids and Silhouettes

Teacher Notes

In Part 6 of *Implementing Investigations in Grade 4,* you will find a set of Teacher Notes that addresses topics and issues applicable to the curriculum as a whole rather than to specific curriculum units. They include the following:

Computational Fluency and Place Value

Computation Algorithms and Methods

Representations and Contexts for Mathematical Work

Foundations of Algebra in the Elementary Grades

Discussing Mathematical Ideas

Racial and Linguistic Diversity in the Classroom: Raising Questions About What Equity in the Math Classroom Means Today

Dialogue Boxes

Teacher Note

Difficulties in Visualizing Silhouettes

Many students do not understand exactly which part of a solid is producing the shape of its silhouette. In some cases—depending on the viewing angle—a silhouette is identical to one of the faces of the solid; in other cases it is not.

For instance, the octagonal prism can make this rectangular silhouette:

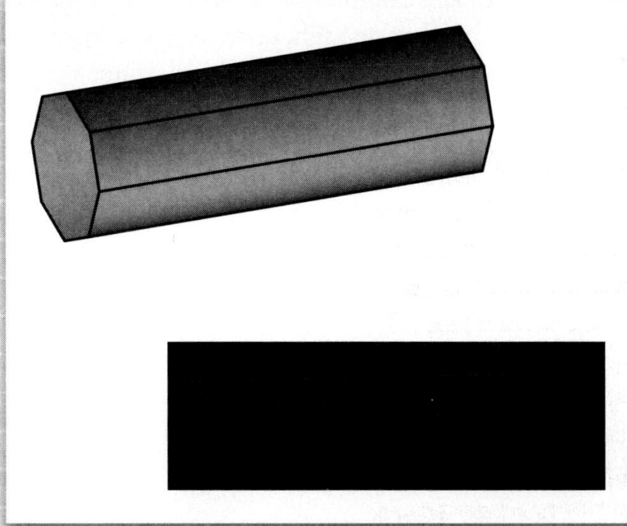

Some students think that the silhouette should be considerably narrower—that it would be identical to one of the prism's rectangular faces. Try this yourself to see the difference.

Other students imagine the silhouette of a cube viewed directly on its edge as a line segment (one of its edges) or a square (one of its faces) rather than a rectangle. To demonstrate that it is a rectangle, place a cube on the overhead with only one of its edges touching the glass. (This silhouette matches Silhouette K on *Student Activity Book* page 5.)

Students may also gain a better understanding of solids and silhouettes by tracing the outline of a solid on an overhead transparency. For example, if students think that the silhouette for the hexagonal prism is produced by one of its faces, they would trace this face on a transparency. They will see their mistake when they place the transparency, along with the solid, on the overhead and compare the drawing with the actual silhouette. The resulting discrepancy will lead students to reevaluate their theory of silhouettes.

As you are showing silhouettes on the overhead, many students will notice a bit of "overhang." For instance, if you place the narrow square prism on the glass on one of its square bases, you might see (depending on where the prism is positioned) not only the silhouette of the base but also parts of the long rectangular faces. Acknowledge this, but tell students that they should think about "perfect" silhouettes—what they would see if they took these objects outside on a sunny day with the sun directly overhead.

Some silhouettes can be produced only by positioning solids on the overhead in specific ways. For example, the cone produces a triangle only if the base is held perpendicular to the overhead glass.

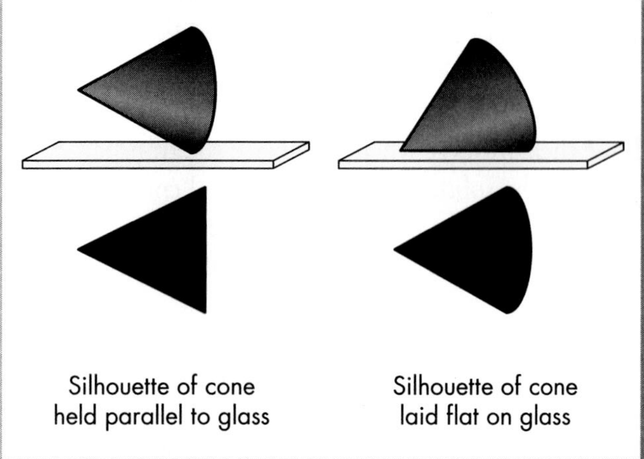

Some students will lay the cone flat on the overhead and claim that it cannot make a triangular silhouette. A demonstration of the parallel position easily convinces most students otherwise. For some students, however, the problem lies deeper. For example, here is how one student thought about the silhouette of a cone as he tried to match it to the shapes on *Student Activity Book* page 5.

Luke: The cone doesn't match any of them [the silhouettes on page 5] because it's curved on the bottom.

Teacher: What about now? [The teacher holds the cone with the base perpendicular to the overhead.]

Luke: No, because I still know it's curved. It's the same thing.

The difficulty here is not simply that the student is confused by the circular overhang. It is a conceptual problem: the student cannot believe that a circular object can produce a straight-sided silhouette such as a triangle. This student needs more experience with viewing silhouettes on the overhead or in direct sunlight.

Teacher Note

Assessment: Match the Silhouettes

Benchmark addressed:

Benchmark 1: Identifying 2-dimensional silhouettes of 3-dimensional solids (e.g., a cone can project a triangular silhouette).

In order to meet the benchmark, students' work should show that they can use the given perspective to identify the following:

- The silhouettes for both the cone and the square pyramid are triangles;
- The silhouette for the cylinder is a square;
- The silhouette for the triangular prism is a rectangle;
- The silhouette for the sphere is a circle.

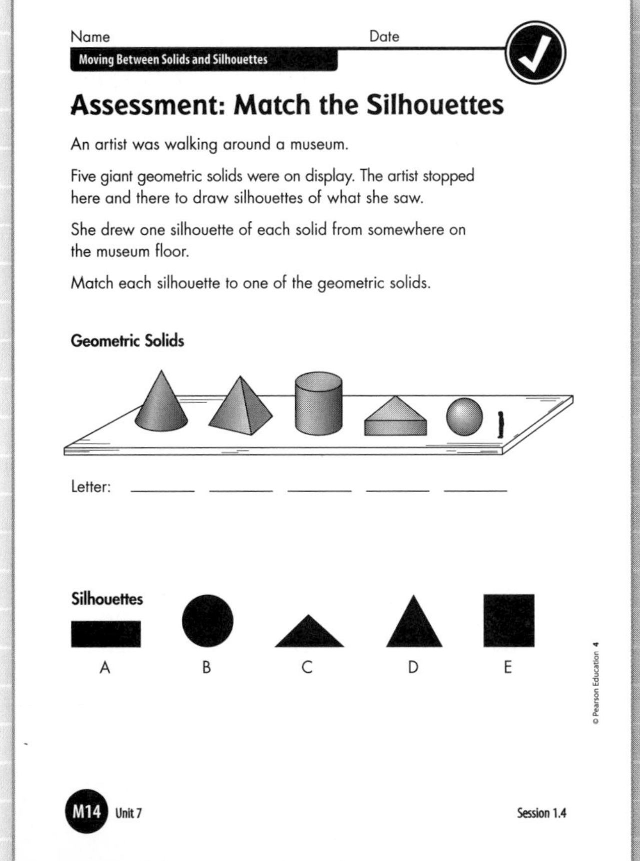

Name Date

Moving Between Solids and Silhouettes

Assessment: Match the Silhouettes

An artist was walking around a museum.

Five giant geometric solids were on display. The artist stopped here and there to draw silhouettes of what she saw.

She drew one silhouette of each solid from somewhere on the museum floor.

Match each silhouette to one of the geometric solids.

Geometric Solids

Letter: ______ ______ ______ ______ ______

Silhouettes

A B C D E

© Pearson Education 4

M14 Unit 7 Session 1.4

▲ Resource Masters, M14

Meeting the Benchmark

Students who meet the benchmark correctly identify the 2-D silhouettes of 3-D solids. Noemi's answers are D, C, E, A, B. She recognizes that, although the silhouettes of the cone and the square pyramid are triangles, the triangle from the cone (D) is taller and narrower than the triangle from the square pyramid (C). Students who meet the benchmark use the correct perspective and are paying attention to both the shape and size of the silhouettes.

Partially Meeting the Benchmark

Students who pay attention to the shape of the silhouette but not the size partially meet the benchmark. Derek's answers are C, D, E, A, B. He recognizes that the cone and the square pyramid both have a triangular silhouette, but does not identify the correct silhouette for each solid. Although Derek is paying attention to the correct perspective and the shape of the silhouette, he is not paying attention to the size.

Other students who partially meet the benchmark have one error in perspective. For example, Richard's answers are D, C, B, A, B. He identifies the circle (B) as the silhouette for the cylinder. Amelia's answers are D, C, E, D, B. She identifies the triangle (D) as the silhouette for the triangular prism. In both of these cases, students are using the perspective of the "top" of the solids not the "front."

Not Meeting the Benchmark

Students who have more than one error in perspective or who have multiple errors in identifying the correct silhouettes do not meet the benchmark. For example, Steve's answers are C, D, B, C, B—he uses a top perspective for the pyramid and prism. Ramona's answers are B, E, A, C, B, which indicate that she is unable to identify the correct perspectives. These students need more experience identifying the silhouettes that are produced by placing different faces of the solids on the overhead projector.

Teacher Note

Interpreting 2-D Diagrams of 3-D Shapes

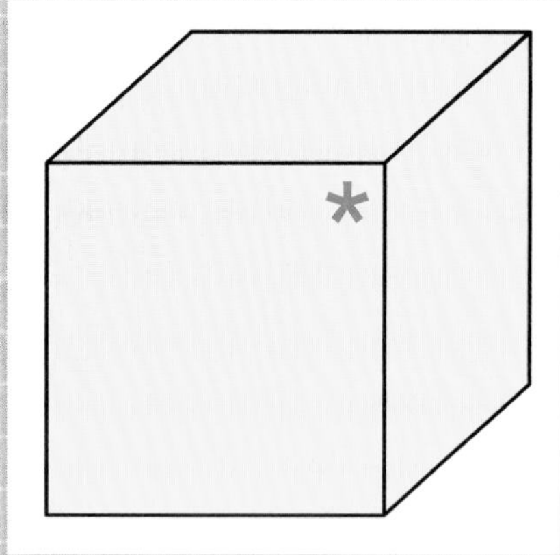

How do you see or interpret this diagram? Most people see it as a picture of a solid. They think of the vertex marked with the asterisk as protruding toward them. Other people see the figure as an inside, upper corner of a room. They think of the vertex with the asterisk as receding away from them. This is a nonstandard view, but it is not incorrect.

Some students may, at first, have difficulties with these activities because they do not see or interpret the diagrams in the standard way. For instance, to make the building numbered 1 on *Student Activity Book* page 17, one student started with the building shown below:

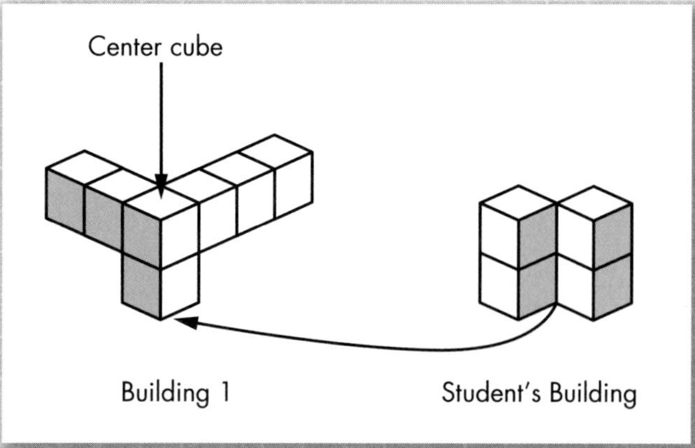

This student was seeing the drawing of the center cube as the inside corner of the room. Thus, she interpreted the entire figure as the upper right-hand corner of a room. As she tried to build what she saw, she constructed the center bottom portion, but then said it was impossible to continue.

Although most students "understand" the diagrams of cube configurations, it is not uncommon for some of them to interpret them in nonstandard ways. Most students with nonstandard interpretations quickly change their ideas when they are made aware that it is not what the artist intended. The student who had trouble with the number 1 building changed her interpretation after she heard other students talk about how they saw it. Other students learn to interpret the diagrams only after spending a great deal of time building different cube configurations from diagrams. In any case, to help all students better understand these 2-D diagrams, it is essential to have them talk together about their interpretations.

Teacher Note

Staying Properly Oriented

After students have made a cube building and are trying to draw its silhouettes, they may pick up their building and turn it without keeping track of which side is the front. This may cause them confusion. After pointing out this potential problem, you might suggest that students keep their building flat on the desktop or table and that they themselves move around to view the building from different sides.

You could also have students use a small toy figure to act out viewing the building from different perspectives. Placing a cube building on a table, students should identify the front of the building and draw a "road" passing in front of it (or use a pencil to represent the road). Then they can place the toy figure looking directly at the front of the building and crouch behind the toy—with their eye level matching that of the toy's—to view the building as the toy does.

Next, students make their toy figure "fly" straight up several feet in front of the building and look down. What does the top of the building look like from this front view? Students then return the toy to its original position and make it "walk" around to the right side of the building. Then they can crouch again to see the right side of the building from the viewpoint of the toy figure.

These activities should help students identify the different views of the cube buildings; a student who is having difficulty may reenact them at any time. However, even when students can correctly identify the different views, they still might not be able to properly visualize the corresponding silhouettes. For these students, always use the overhead to clarify what the building's actual silhouette looks like.

A student uses a pencil as a "road" to identify the front of the cube building.

Teacher Note

Integrating Three Views: How Students Try to Do It

When students construct an object by looking only at three silhouettes (as on *Student Activity Book* page 30), they must combine the information from the three different views, synthesizing it to form one comprehensive view of an object. This process of integrating information is important not only in geometry, but also in mathematics and reasoning in general.

As students work on these tasks, you will observe different levels of sophistication in their skills.

- Some students recognize that integration is needed but are unable to achieve it mentally. Instead, they look at one of the silhouettes and speculate about what the building will look like, judging solely from that single view. They then make a building to match that silhouette and physically check to see whether it matches the other two views. If it does not, they make successive changes to the building—taking away a cube here, adding one there—in an attempt to make it match all three views. As these students work, they focus on only one view at a time.

- Some students first make a building that matches one view but they seem to expect that their building will require changes. They reflect on any changes before making them, trying to figure out how each change will affect the different views. These students are often able to anticipate the effects of changes before they perform them. This approach, however, is one of coordination rather than integration.

- Some students truly integrate the information given in the three silhouettes. They approach the problem by integrating the three views to make a mental model of the cube building. This model may be something like the isometric drawings they have seen throughout this unit. These students then construct the building from their mental image.

Students who are having difficulty integrating the different views simply need more practice with this type of problem. For many students, this is a problem they have never before encountered. Thus, they will need many such experiences over a span of several years before they become adept at mentally integrating different views into a single model.

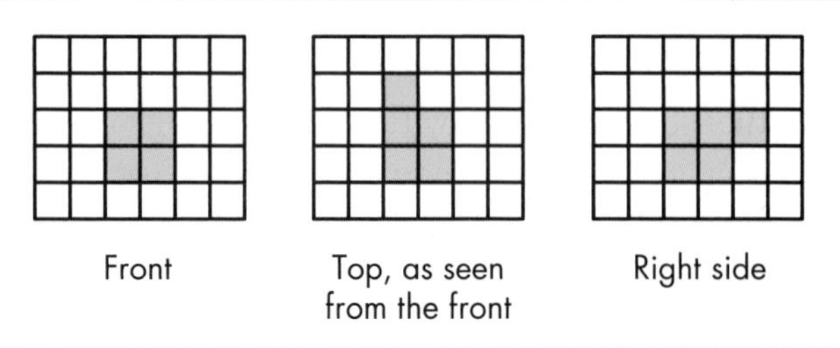

Strategies for Finding the Number of Cubes in 3-D Arrays

For students to determine how many cubes are in a 3-D array, they must mentally construct an image or model of the set of cubes. Students have been observed to do this in a variety of ways. Some of these ways are listed below, in order of the students' increasing ability to see the whole and its parts in an organized manner. You will see your students' progress from less organized to more organized methods as the unit progresses. However, the progress may be slow, and students may approach different tasks with different levels of understanding.

Seeing Arrays as Unstructured Sets

Whether given an actual cube package (a rectangular prism), a picture of a cube package, or the box that contains that package, some students see no organization of the cubes. In this case, students usually count cubes one by one and almost always lose track of their count. For these students, the task is like counting a large number of randomly arranged objects.

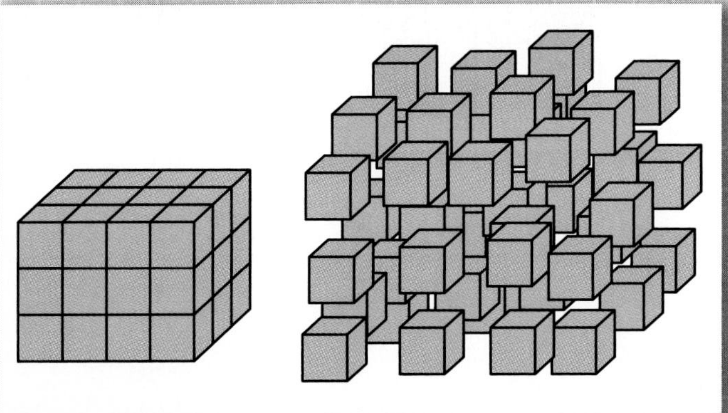

Seeing Arrays in Terms of Sides or Faces

Many students approach 3-D arrays of cubes by thinking only about the sides of the rectangular prism formed by the cubes. These students might count all or some of the cube faces (squares) that appear on the six sides. With this method, edge cubes are often counted more than once, and cubes in the center are missed.

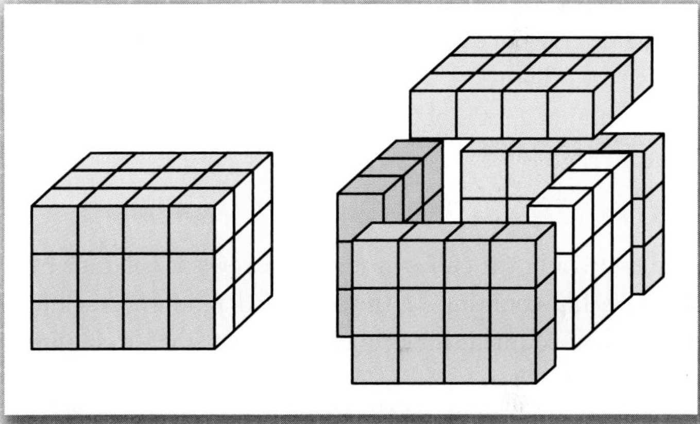

Thus, a box of 36 cubes ($3 \times 4 \times 3$) might be counted as 54 cubes—the front, back, and top as 12 each; the right and left sides as 9 each.

Most students with this "sides" conceptualization use it consistently, whether they are looking at pictures of boxes, box patterns, or the actual cube configurations. Students who see cube arrays in terms of their faces do not necessarily think of arrays as hollow; they simply think that their method counts all of the cubes, inside and out.

Seeing Arrays as Having Outside and Inside Parts

Students who take this approach try to count both the outside and the inside of the 3-D array—sometimes correctly, but more often incorrectly. They attempt to visualize the entire package and account for each cube.

- **Correct Counting** One student counted the cubes visible on the front face (12) and then counted those on the right side that had not already been counted (6). She then pointed to the remaining cubes on the top, and for each, counted cubes in columns of 3: 1, 2, 3; 4, 5, 6; . . . 16, 17, 18. She then added 12, 6, and 18.
- **Incorrect Counting** One student counted all of the outside cube faces of this same array, getting 66. He then said that there were 2 cubes in the middle. This gave him at a total of 68.

Seeing Arrays in Terms of Rows or Columns

Students count the cubes in successive rows or columns by 1s or by skip-counting. In the strategy diagrammed below, the student counted three cubes for each of the six columns.

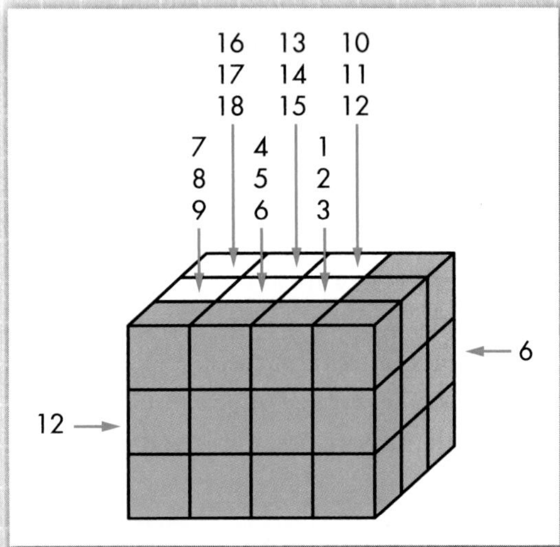

Seeing Arrays in Terms of Layers

Students determine the number of cubes in one layer and then multiply or use repeated addition to account for all of the layers. The layers can be vertical or horizontal, and students often use one of the visible faces in a picture as a representation of a layer. Other students look at a box pattern, see the bottom as representing a layer, and then determine the number of layers by looking at the sides of the pattern. Many students who use layering often count the cubes in a layer 1 by 1.

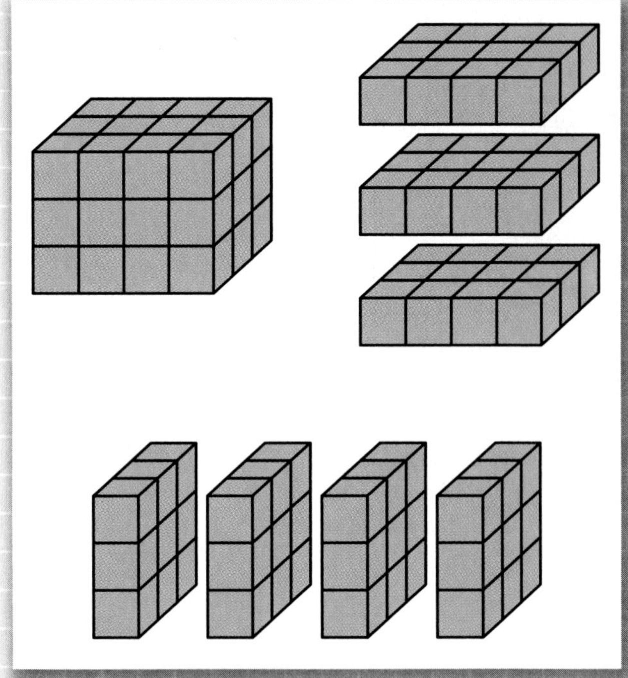

Seeing Arrays as Layers Described by Dimensions

Some students understand how dimensions can be used to describe and count the cubes in an array.

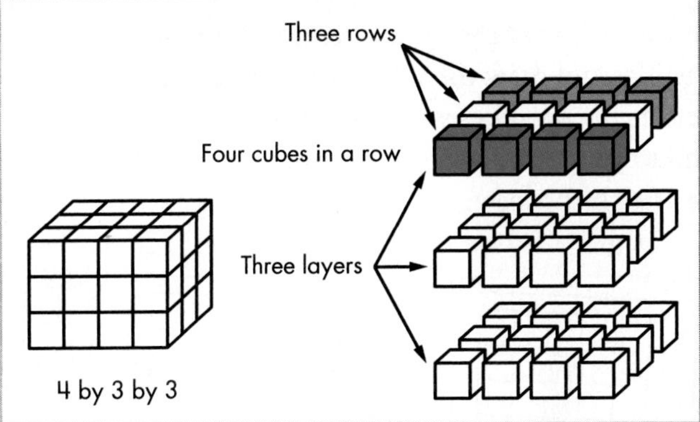

Students might reason that the length gives the number of cubes in a row and the width gives the number of rows in a layer, so the number of cubes in a layer is the product of the length and width. Because the height gives the number of layers, they multiply the number of cubes in a layer by the height to find the total number of cubes in the array. Not all students refer to the dimensions as length, width, and height.

The Learning Process

Students gradually progress to more powerful ways of conceptualizing cube configurations as they have repeated experiences with trying to find the volume first, building boxes, filling them with cubes, enumerating the cubes, and discussing their ideas with classmates.

Expected Progress

Do not expect all students to be able to think in terms of layers by the end of this investigation. They do work similar to this in Grade 5. It is sufficient if they have developed a strategy that gives correct answers. Despite your efforts to promote it, students may not be able to arrange cubes in layers. Also, be cautious about pushing students to use dimensions. Too much emphasis on this can pressure students to adopt a numerical procedure (multiplying the dimensions) that they do not understand, causing them to abandon a visual method that makes sense to them.

End-of-Unit Assessment

Problem 1

Benchmark addressed:

Benchmark 2: Draw 2-dimensional representations showing different perspectives of a 3-dimensional object.

In order to meet the benchmark, students' work should show that they can:

- Use the same orientation to draw the correct silhouettes of the front, top, and right side of a solid.

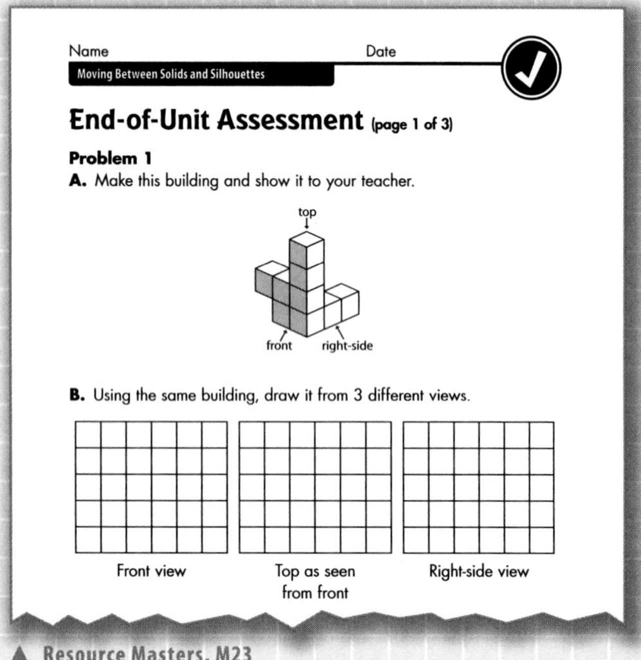

Name Date

Moving Between Solids and Silhouettes

End-of-Unit Assessment (page 1 of 3)

Problem 1

A. Make this building and show it to your teacher.

top

front right-side

B. Using the same building, draw it from 3 different views.

Front view | Top as seen from front | Right-side view

▲ Resource Masters, M23

Note: In this assessment, students are asked first to make the building and show it to the teacher. It is important to make sure that the buildings are correctly built—*with no hidden cubes*—or it will be difficult to assess whether students have drawn the correct silhouettes. The descriptions of student work below assume that buildings were made correctly.

Meeting the Benchmark

Students who use the same orientation for all three drawings and draw the silhouettes correctly meet the benchmark. Damian's work shows the correct silhouettes based on the orientation that is shown on the assessment sheet.

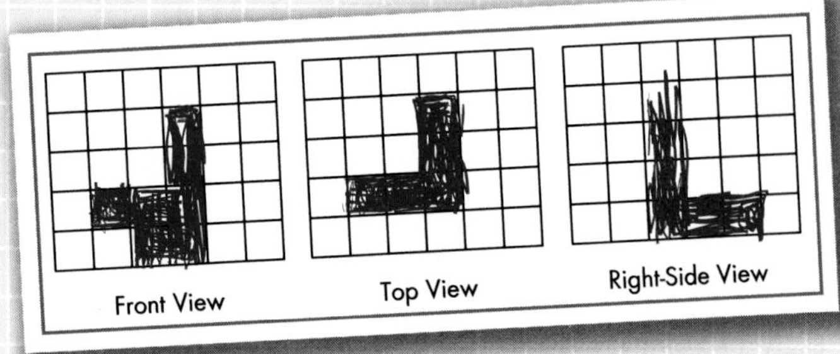

Damien's Work

It is possible for students to use a different orientation from what is given and still meet the benchmark. Venetta's work is an example of this. She chooses to use the "L" shape as her front view. With that orientation as the front of her cube building, Venetta correctly draws the top and right-side views.

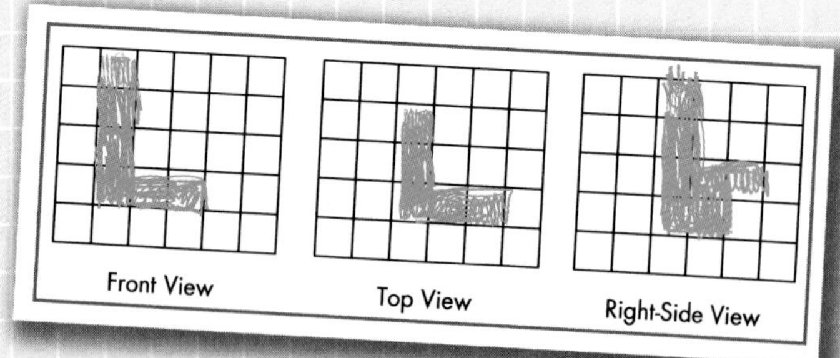

Venetta's Work

Yuki's work shows that he understands perspective, orientation, and silhouettes. However, he makes an error in the drawing of his top view. Yuki's error of one cube in one view is minor, and therefore he meets the benchmark.

Yuki should be asked to check each view carefully to see whether he can correct the error himself.

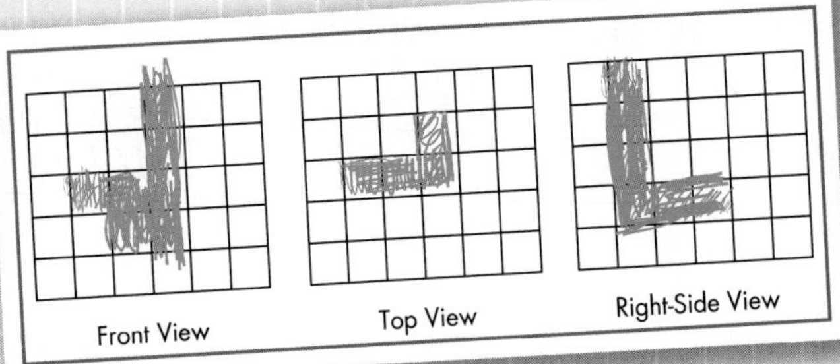

Yuki's Work

Partially Meeting the Benchmark

Students partially meet the benchmark if they use the same orientation and draw two of the three silhouettes correctly. Benson correctly draws the front and right-side views. His top view, however, is incorrect. Benson draws the center square as connected diagonally to the left and right side of the building. This reveals that either he does not understand what the top view should be or he is having problems translating between 3-D and 2-D objects. The teacher might ask Benson what he was thinking about as he drew the top view and have him use the overhead projector to see what the silhouette would look like.

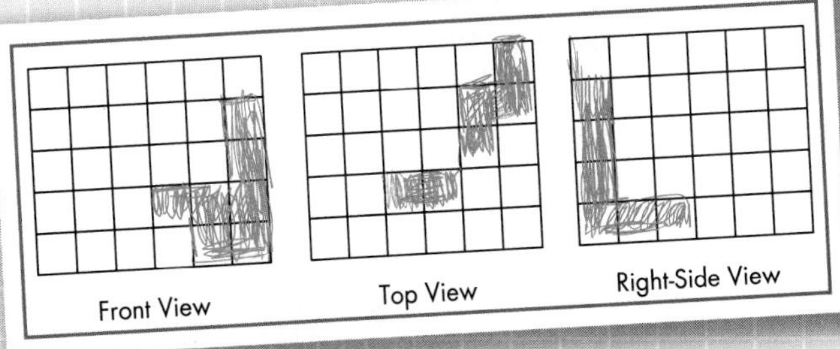

Benson's Work

Not Meeting the Benchmark

Students do not meet the benchmark if they use more than one orientation to draw the silhouettes and/or cannot correctly draw the silhouettes. Luke seems unable to see the correct perspective for drawing the silhouettes. His front view would be correct except that he adds two cubes to the right of the object. His top view shows only one cube, and it is not clear (without asking) how he visualizes the right-side view. Luke needs more experience with staying properly oriented. He would benefit from using a toy figure and crouching down to see the correct perspective as well as from using the overhead to see the silhouettes.

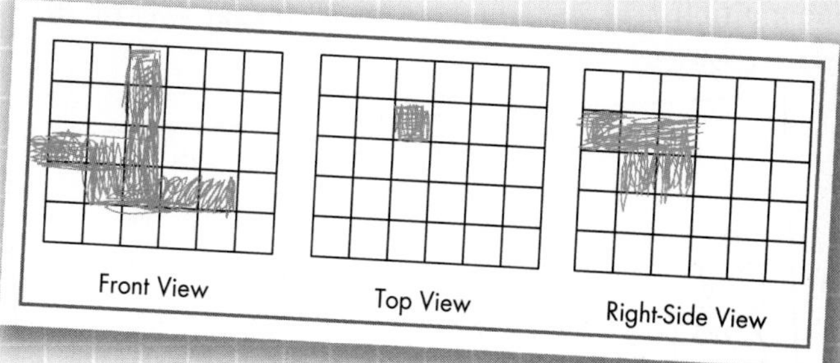

Luke's Work

Problem 2

Benchmark addressed:

Benchmark 3: Find the volume of cube buildings and rectangular prisms.

In order to meet the benchmark, students' work should show that they can:

- Determine the correct number of cubes in the given structure;
- Recognize that they are working with 3-D objects (cubes) and not 2-D objects (squares).

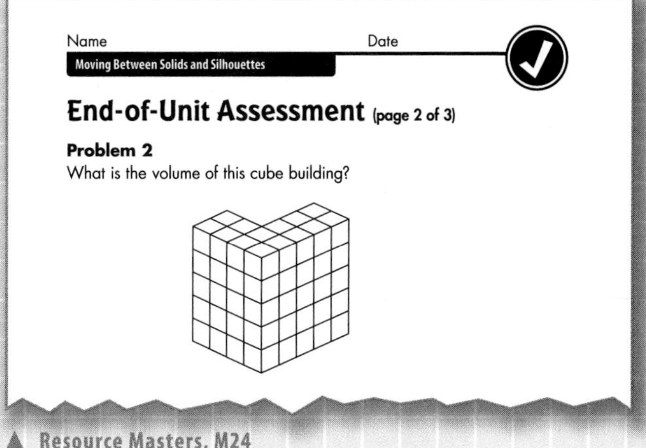
Name Date

Moving Between Solids and Silhouettes

End-of-Unit Assessment (page 2 of 3)

Problem 2

What is the volume of this cube building?

▲ Resource Masters, M24

Meeting the Benchmark

Students who have the correct answer of 70 cubes and whose work explains their solution meet the benchmark.

Cheyenne recognizes that each column of this object contains 5 cubes and that there are 14 columns altogether. She multiplies 14 × 5 and gets the correct answer of 70.

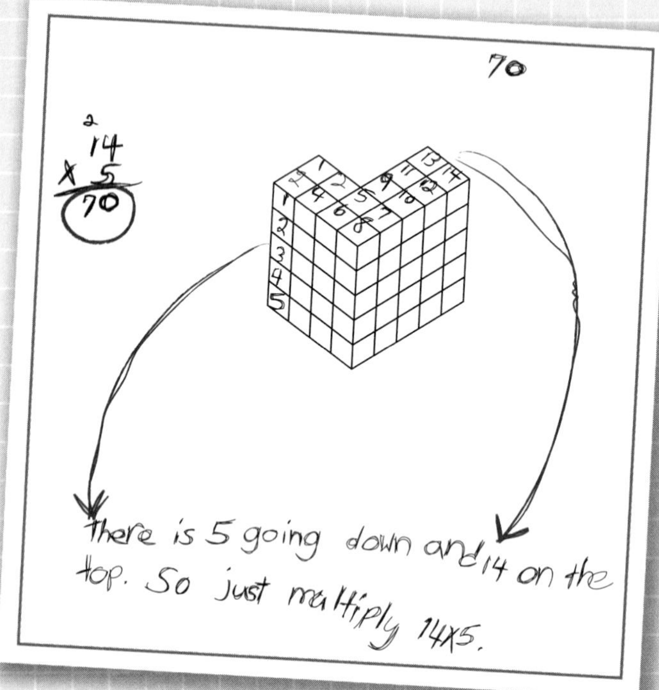

Cheyenne's Work

Tonya circles groups of 2 columns and notates them as 5 × 2. She circles 6 such groups, and indicates a final group of 5 × 2. She multiplies 5 × 2 × 7 (5 × 2 = 10, 7 × 10 = 70) to get the correct answer.

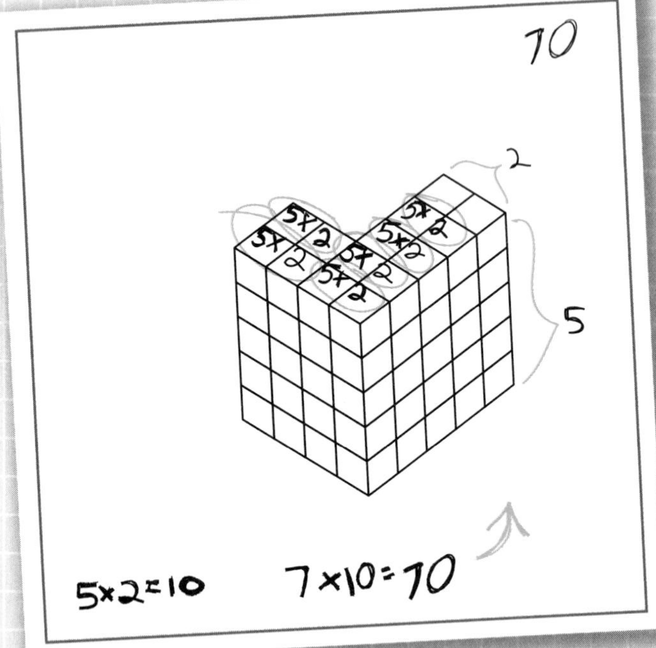

Tonya's Work

Students who correctly count every cube (including those that cannot be seen) also meet the benchmark. Some students also think about the object as a prism with dimensions of 4 × 5 × 5 and then determine that the piece added to "complete" the rectangular prism is three groups of 10 cubes, so the answer is 100 − 30, or 70 cubes.

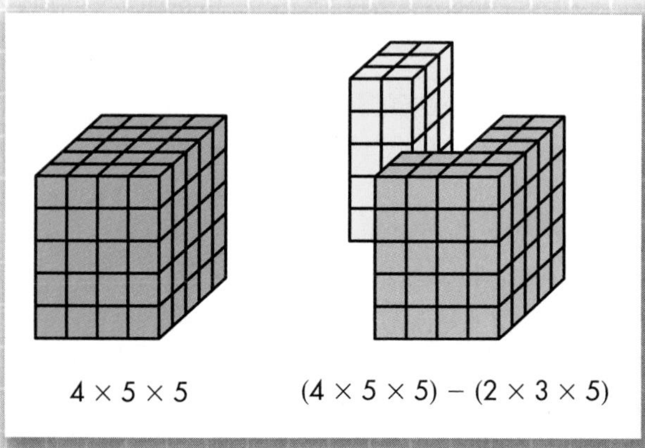

Partially Meeting the Benchmark

Students who are unable to count all of the cubes, but still show some understanding of volume, partially meet the benchmark. Ursula counts only the cubes that can be seen, but she is also careful not to double-count cubes. For example, in thinking about the "top" of the structure, Ursula recognizes that she has already counted 8 of those cubes in her count of each side. Thus, there are only 6 cubes that still need to be counted. Ursula does understand that she is counting cubes and not squares. She should be asked whether there are cubes that cannot be seen, and if so, how many.

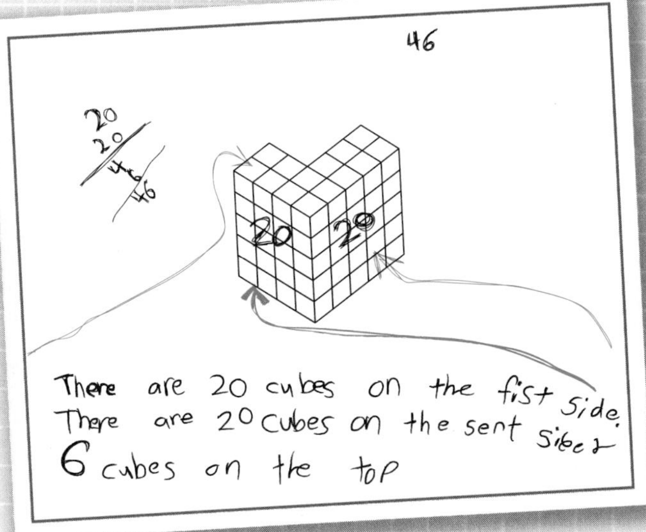

Ursula's Work

Not Meeting the Benchmark

Students who double-count cubes, miss cubes, or count only the faces do not meet the benchmark. When Jake counts the "sides" of this structure, he does not double-count the cubes that are shared. However, when he counts the top cubes, he double-counts the 8 cubes to get an answer of 54 cubes. Jake should be asked whether there are any cubes he counted more than once, and whether there are any cubes that cannot be seen.

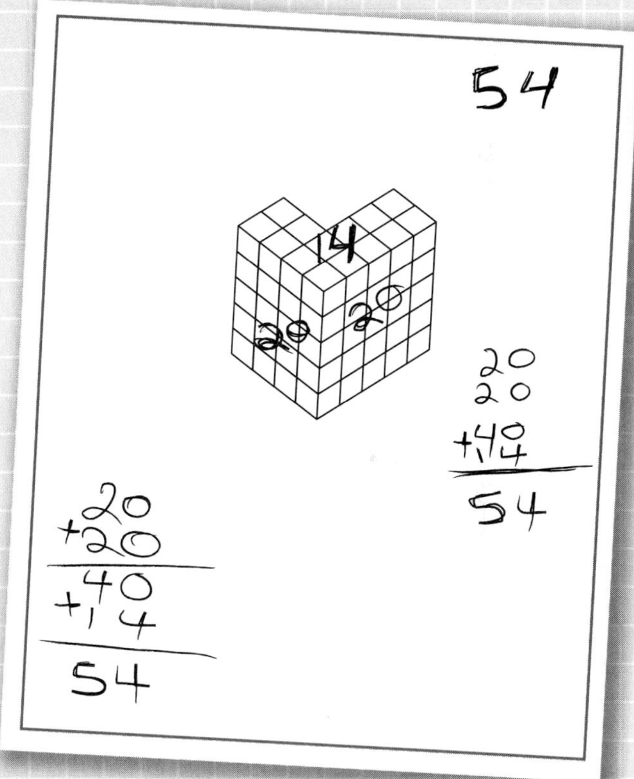

Jake's Work

Students who get 59 as an answer count all of the visible faces and do not consider that each square represents the face of a cube.

Problem 3

Benchmark addressed:

Benchmark 3: Find the volume of cube boxes and rectangular prisms.

In order to meet the benchmark, students' work should show that they can:

- Determine what the box pattern would look like if it were cut out and formed into a box;
- Find the volume of a rectangular prism.

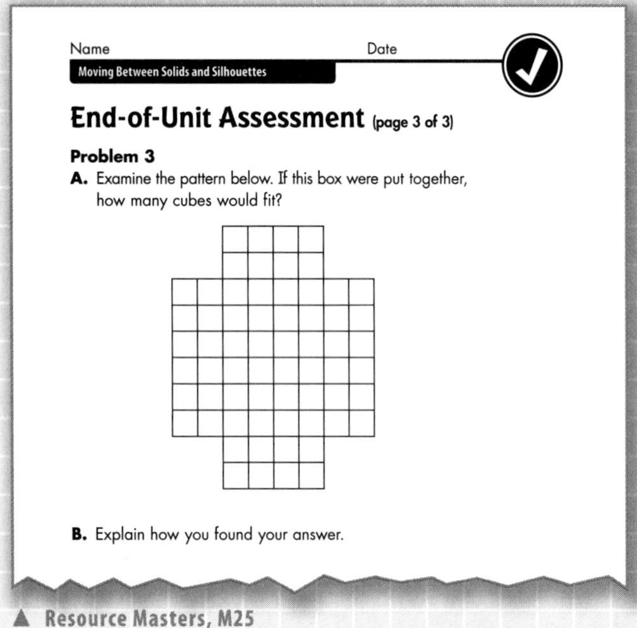

Name Date

Moving Between Solids and Silhouettes

End-of-Unit Assessment (page 3 of 3)

Problem 3

A. Examine the pattern below. If this box were put together, how many cubes would fit?

B. Explain how you found your answer.

▲ Resource Masters, M25

The expectation is that most students will meet the benchmark for this activity, although some may need guidance correcting errors. Others may need additional experience to develop their understanding of the structure of box patterns and the rectangular prisms that fit within them.

Meeting the Benchmark

Students who determine that the bottom layer of the prism contains 24 cubes (6 × 4) and that there are 2 layers (for a total of 48 cubes) meet the benchmark. Lucy numbers the outside edges of the pattern and identifies the 6 and the 4 as the dimensions of the bottom of the box and the 2 as the number of layers. She multiplies 6 × 4 to get 24 and then multiplies by 2 to get the correct answer of 48 cubes.

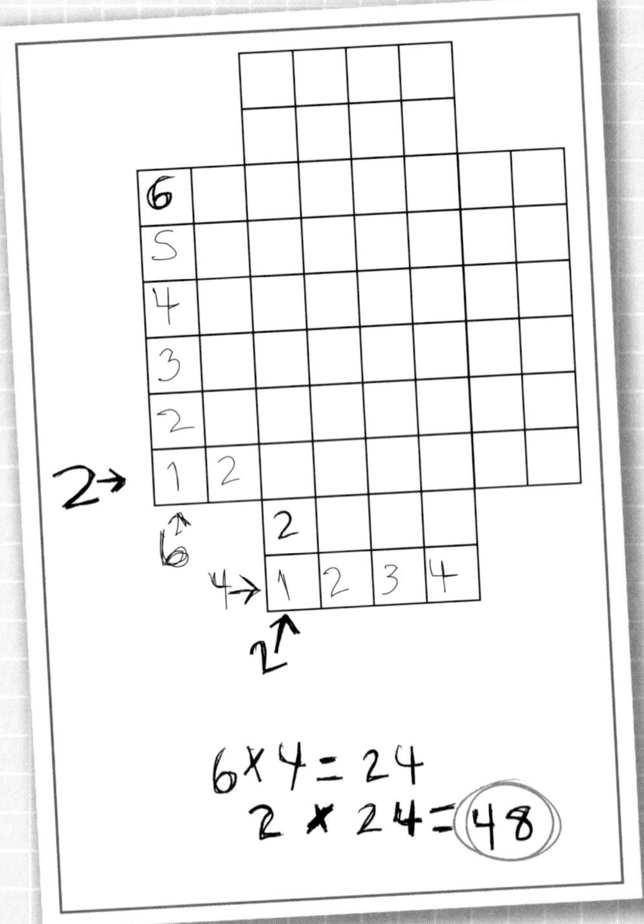

Lucy's Work

Nadeem's written explanation shows a solid understanding of finding volume. He describes the dimensions of center as being 6 × 4 and the height of the box 2 units for total of 48 cubes.

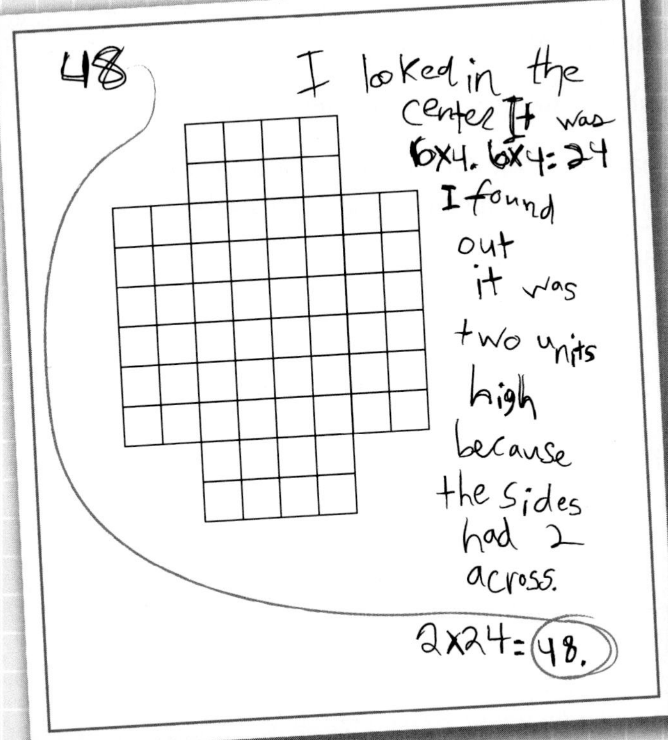

Nadeem's Work

Partially Meeting the Benchmark

It is possible that some students understand that to find the volume of 3-D cube arrays, you find the number of cubes in one layer and multiply it by the number of layers. Nevertheless, these students may make a computation error. For example, a student might incorrectly say that the bottom layer is "6 × 4, which is 28." Because there are two layers, the student would find a total of 56 cubes. Because the answer is incorrect, consider students with computation errors as partially meeting the benchmark. However, these students should have the opportunity to correct the computation error. If they do, they should be considered as meeting the benchmark.

Not Meeting the Benchmark

Students who count only the squares shown do not meet the benchmark. Bill's work shows that he understands that 6 × 4 is the bottom of the box, but he then counts each square in the sides as well. Bill does not understand that he is working with 3-dimensional objects and that the squares in the pattern represent the outside faces of the cubes in the rectangular prism. He needs more experience in cutting out patterns, making the cube arrays, and making his own patterns for a given number of cubes.

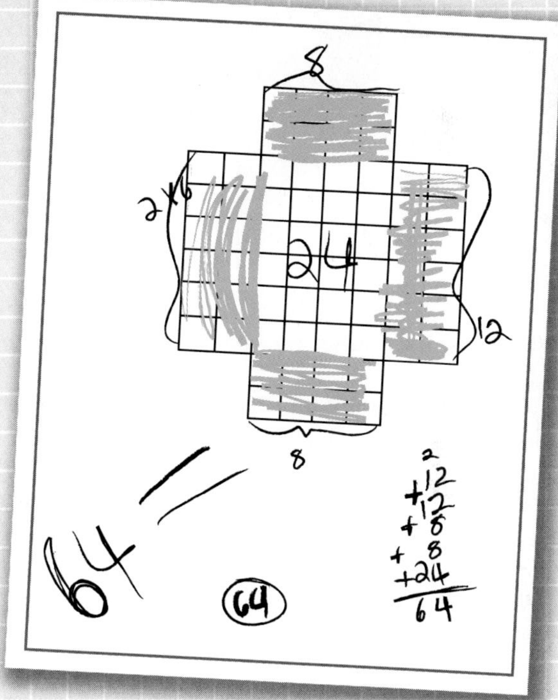

Bill's Work

Dialogue Box

Seeing Cube Buildings in Our Minds

The teacher has shown Image 2 from *Quick Images* 3-D (T74) twice for 3 seconds each time. He has also given students enough time to construct and then revise their buildings. The teacher then turns on the overhead for a third time, leaving it on so that students can compare their buildings with the image. He leads a class discussion on how students made the building.

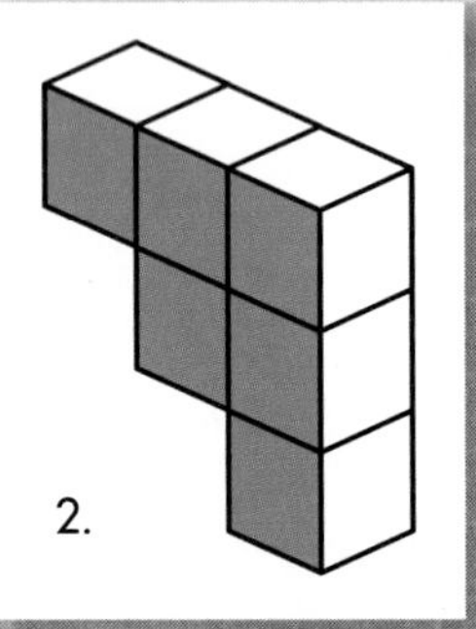

Teacher: How did you see the cube building in your mind?

Luke: Three cubes going up this way, two this way [motioning with hands], one at the bottom.

Jill: I pretended there was an L on the top and a box in the middle.

Andrew: If you turned this upside down, it would be like steps.

LaTanya: If you turn it this way, it looks like a flower.

Teacher: What did you look for when I showed the picture the second time?

Helena: Where it turns.

Yuki: How many blocks on the arms.

Teacher: How did you know how many cubes to use for this part? [points to the longer arm]

Alejandro: I counted.

Anna: I could just see it.

The teacher notes the different organizations students give to their images. Luke counts cubes in different parts and Jill sees simpler geometric shapes such as an L [a right angle] and a box [a square]. Andrew and LaTanya see the image as whole objects. The teacher realizes that these are all important aspects of decomposing the shape to make the entire building. It is important for students to discuss their organization strategies. Hearing such strategies described helps students look for similar organizations in the next *Quick Images* picture.

Good Thinking Does Not Always Result in Correct Answers

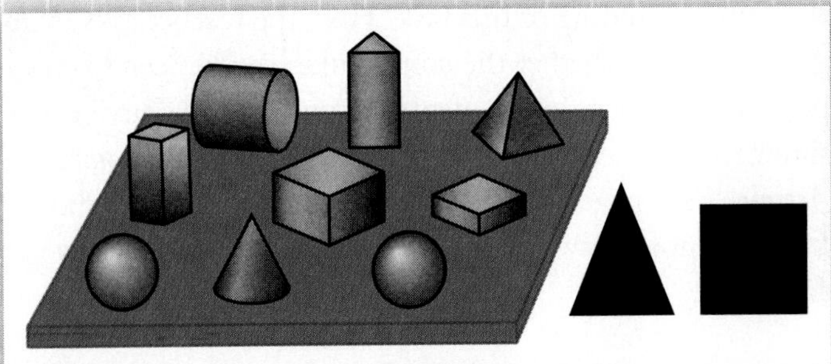

The class has been working on *Student Activity Book* page 11. Now they are talking about silhouette pair 2 (as shown above). They are trying to decide from which points in the landscape this pair of silhouettes can be seen.

Derek: I think point B works because you can see the front of the square, and if you tilt your head up you can see a triangle—but you don't see the whole entire triangle, just the top of the triangle. (He draws a triangle in the air.)

Teacher: Can you show that to us on Landscape 2?

Derek places a tiny upright figure at point B in the landscape his group built from the wooden solids. The figure directly faces the cube in the center.

Derek: Point B is right there. See, if you focus, you can see this. [He moves his finger from the eyes of the figure to the closest face of the cube.] You can see the square. Then, if you tilt your head up, you can see the top of the triangle. [He places one finger across the top of the cone, about three-quarters of the way up from the bottom, forming a triangle.]

Teacher: The top of the cone?

Derek: Yeah, that's a triangle.

Teacher: That's true. But it's not the whole triangle we see in the silhouette pair—is that all right?

Derek: Yes, we're just supposed to see a triangle.

Teacher: Class, what do you think about Derek's reasoning? Do you agree?

Most of the class members say yes.

Teacher: Everyone agrees that our toy figure will see a triangle if it sees the top of the cone. But how can we be sure that it sees the cone? How can we tell for sure?

Derek: Look, it sees from here to here [quickly drawing a line in the air from the toy's eyes to the upper portion of the cone].

Ursula: Wait a minute. [She goes around the table and crouches directly behind the toy figure, with her eyes at the same level as those of the toy.] I can't see the cone.

Derek: Come on, let me see. [He gets in the same position as Ursula.] I see it.

Ursula [returns to her crouching position]**:** Well, I see it if I put my head this high, but I don't see if it I put my head lower.

Teacher: What do the rest of you think?

After several more students take the viewing position of Ursula, the class decides that how you see the triangle depends on how high your eyes are. They conclude that Derek's answer and reasoning should be considered correct. The teacher then returns to the issue of size.

Teacher: While you were stooping down and looking at the solids, how did the sizes of the square and triangle compare?

Yuki: They were different. The triangle was small.

Teacher: So does the toy figure see the triangle and square in pair 2?

Derek: Yes, it is a triangle.

Yuki: But it's a small triangle. It's not like the picture.

Most, but not all, of the students say that the triangle is too small and that you cannot really see the large triangle silhouette in pair 2 by looking at the cone from point B.

Although the teacher recognizes that Derek's overall answer is incorrect, she wants to encourage Derek's thinking and help him refine it. Derek has a solid understanding of geometric perspective. He knows that a cone will project a triangle, and he communicates clearly enough to convince most of his classmates. The teacher is pleased with this, but she also wants Derek and the rest of the class to deepen their understanding of this task. First, the teacher asks them all to consider whether the cone could even be seen from point B. She then asks students to consider the size of the silhouette and whether it would match what is on *Student Activity Book* page 11. The teacher uses what is right about Derek's initial answer to help students look more closely at the task.

Dialogue Box

Describing Our Building Silhouettes

Students have built the cube buildings and drawn the front, top, and side silhouettes. In this discussion, the teacher wants to highlight misconceptions that often occur during this activity.

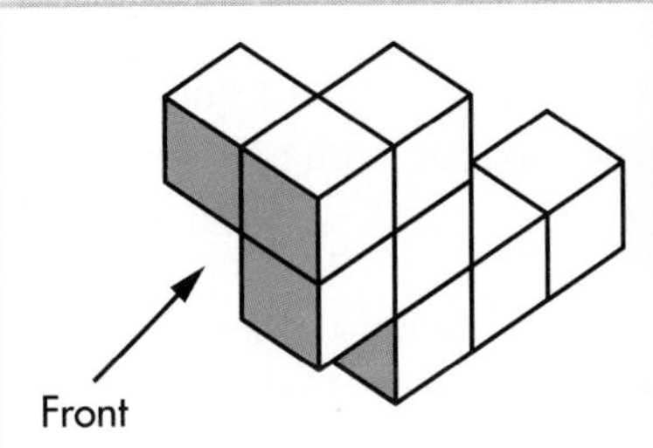

Teacher: Derek, tell us how you're visualizing the front silhouette of this figure. How would you draw it?

Derek: Two squares going across. One coming down from the square on the right.

The teacher draws:

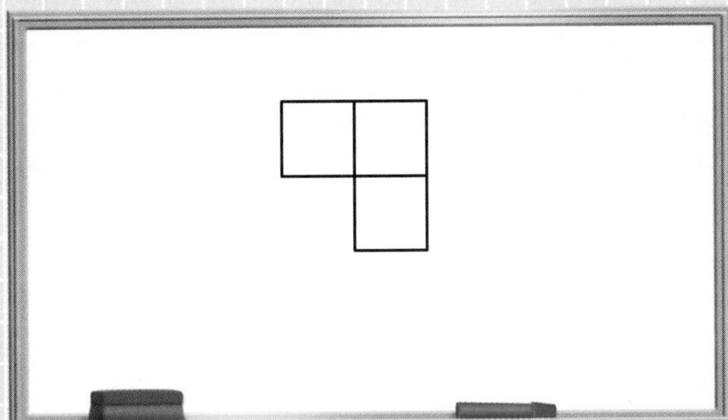

Teacher: Did anyone draw a different silhouette?

Yuson: Mine was just like Derek's, but it has two coming down on the right.

The teacher draws:

Teacher: We have two different versions of the front silhouette. Why?

Sabrina: I think Derek forgot to draw the back cube.

Teacher: What do you think about that, Derek?

Derek: I think Yuson's drawing is right. When I look at my building, it looks like hers. It just confuses me when the cubes are like on different levels. You know what I mean? That one cube is behind the ones I drew.

Teacher: That is hard to remember. Let's check it out on the overhead projector.

The teacher positions the cube building to confirm that Yuson's suggestion for the front silhouette is correct.

Teacher: Now let's try the top-view silhouette. What does it look like? How should I draw it?

As each student describes the silhouette, the teacher draws it on the board.

Amelia: Two cubes across and one on the top right.

Noemi: Four in a straight line [motions vertically] and one coming out at the bottom on the left.

Emaan: Four across [motions horizontally] and one on top, at the left.

The teacher now has three different top-views drawn.

Teacher: What do people think about these different answers?

Marisol: I think that Amelia might not have drawn the back two cubes.

Teacher: Will these two cubes show up in the silhouette? This is the same problem Derek was having earlier.

Amelia: I don't know. Could we try it on the projector?

The teacher places the cube building on the overhead projector so that the correct top silhouette projects onto the screen.

Amelia: Yes, you can see them.

Venetta: Noemi is right [referring to the middle picture above]. That's what I had, too.

Ursula: The drawing on the right is from the side; it's not from the front.

Teacher: Is it a top silhouette?

Ursula: Sure. It's really the same one; it's just turned around. It's the top, but from a side-view, not the front-view.

Teacher: Good. So Emaan's silhouette is a top-view; it's just not from the front. Make sure that you use the correct perspective when you draw your silhouettes.

The teacher carefully listens to the vocabulary students use to describe their silhouettes, noting their use of words such as *across, down, bottom, top, straight, left,* and *right.* The teacher is pleased with the students' precision in describing the silhouettes. She pushes Derek's and Amelia's thinking, helping them understand that they are missing the recessed cubes, which is a common error in this work. Another common mistake occurs when students draw correct silhouettes but use an incorrect perspective. The teacher uses the overhead because he or she realizes that some students still have to see the silhouette to be convinced.

Dialogue Box

Common Student Strategies for Doubling

During the Math Workshop, students work on *Student Activity Book* page 47. The teacher watches and interacts with students as they think about the problems on this page. The teacher stops to watch Kimberly and Enrique, who are working together.

Kimberly and Enrique make a box that is 2 × 3 × 4 and fill it with a package of cubes that has the same dimensions.

Enrique: We have to double the number of cubes, so I think we should double each dimension. What would the new dimensions be?

Kimberly: 4 × 6 × 8?

Enrique: [Looks at the prism they have made.] So right now it's 4 high, and we need to make it 8 high. [The students add cubes. Enrique turns the prism onto its side so that it is now three cubes high.] Now we have to build this side up, so it's 6 high.

Teacher: You're trying to double the number of cubes, right? How could you figure out how many cubes are in the original cube package by looking at the dimensions?

Enrique: The bottom layer would be 6, and there would be 4 layers, so it's 24.

Teacher: What would twice that many be?

Kimberly: 24 doubled is 48.

Teacher: So you're making a box now that is 4 × 6 × 8. How many cubes would that be?

Enrique: The bottom layer would be 4 × 6, that's 24. And 8 layers would be [uses calculator to find 24 × 8] 192. Wow!

Kimberly: Yeah, that's way too many. It's a lot more than doubled. I think we did something wrong.

Teacher: Maybe it would help if you go back and look at the first box you built. Try to use it to help you think about a new box that holds twice as many cubes.

Kimberly and Enrique begin working again, and the teacher moves on to watch other students. She asks Andrew how he doubled the number of cubes.

Andrew: I knew it needed to be 48 cubes. I kept drawing patterns until I found one that held 48 cubes. I know it's double because I filled it with 48 cubes.

Teacher: What are the dimensions of your new package? Do the new dimensions have anything to do with the dimensions of the original box? Or would the dimensions of the original box help you figure out how to double the number of cubes?

The teacher leaves Andrew to think about this and moves on to Sabrina and Lucy.

Sabrina: I made 2 packages of cubes that were 2 × 3 × 4. I put them next to each other and that made a package that was 4 × 3 × 4. Then Lucy noticed what I was doing and said that I could put them together another way.

Lucy: So we put them together and made a new package that was 2 × 6 × 4. And then the last way we did it was a package that was 2 × 3 × 8.

[The two students demonstrate the 3 different positions for their two packages.]

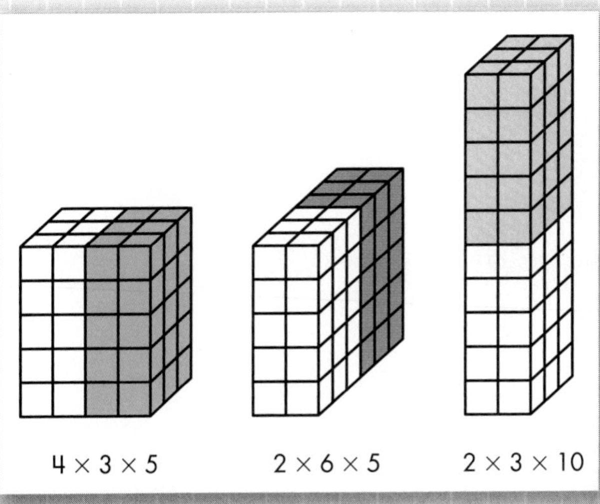

Teacher: That's interesting. What if the original box were $3 \times 3 \times 5$? Do you think you could figure out a way to double the number of cubes without actually building the packages and putting them side-by-side?

As the teacher circulates around the room, she initially encourages the students to think about the problem spatially. She asks students how they can use the cubes or the box patterns to help determine dimensions for new boxes that hold double the number of cubes. She notices that Kimberly and Enrique are focusing only on the dimensions and redirects them to think about the total number of cubes. The teacher knows that all students need opportunities to test their ideas concretely using patterns and cubes. She encourages Lucy and Sabrina to start thinking more abstractly about the problem.

Student Math Handbook

The *Student Math Handbook* pages related to this unit are pictured on the following pages. This book is designed to be used flexibly: as a resource for students doing classwork, as a book students can take home for reference while doing homework and playing math games with their families, and as a reference for families to better understand the work their children are doing in class.

When students take the *Student Math Handbook* home, they and their families can discuss these pages together to reinforce or enhance students' understanding of the mathematical concepts and games in this unit.

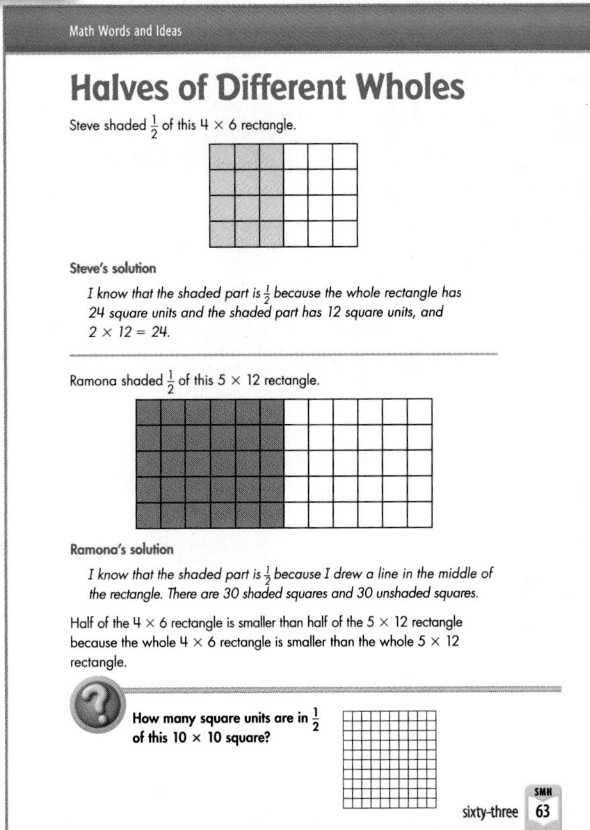

Math Words and Ideas

Halves of Different Wholes

Steve shaded $\frac{1}{2}$ of this 4×6 rectangle.

Steve's solution

I know that the shaded part is $\frac{1}{2}$ because the whole rectangle has 24 square units and the shaded part has 12 square units, and $2 \times 12 = 24$.

Ramona shaded $\frac{1}{2}$ of this 5×12 rectangle.

Ramona's solution

I know that the shaded part is $\frac{1}{2}$ because I drew a line in the middle of the rectangle. There are 30 shaded squares and 30 unshaded squares.

Half of the 4×6 rectangle is smaller than half of the 5×12 rectangle because the whole 4×6 rectangle is smaller than the whole 5×12 rectangle.

How many square units are in $\frac{1}{2}$ of this 10×10 square?

sixty-three SMH 63

Math Words and Ideas, p. 63

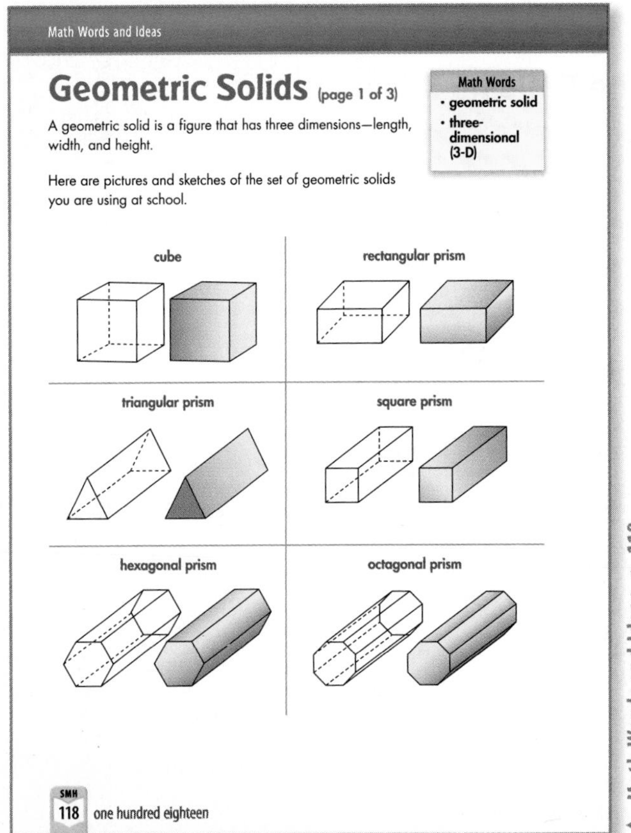

Math Words and Ideas

Geometric Solids (page 1 of 3)

Math Words
- **geometric solid**
- **three-dimensional (3-D)**

A geometric solid is a figure that has three dimensions—length, width, and height.

Here are pictures and sketches of the set of geometric solids you are using at school.

SMH 118 one hundred eighteen

Math Words and Ideas, p. 118

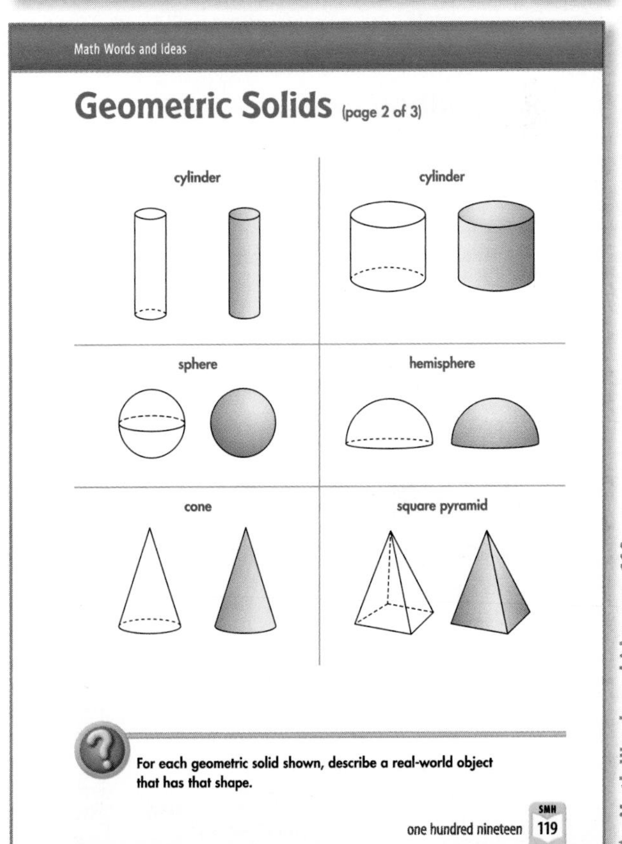

Math Words and Ideas

Geometric Solids (page 2 of 3)

For each geometric solid shown, describe a real-world object that has that shape.

one hundred nineteen SMH 119

Math Words and Ideas, p. 119

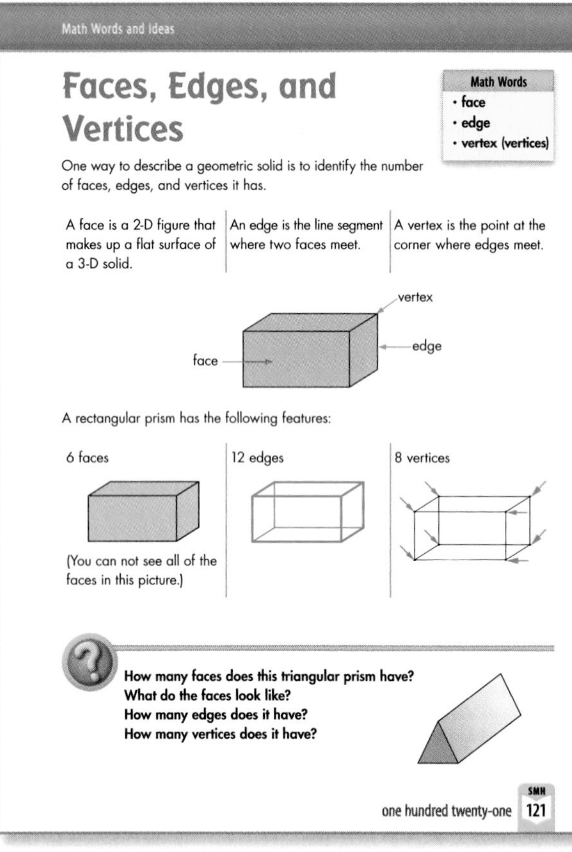

Math Words and Ideas

Faces, Edges, and Vertices

Math Words
- face
- edge
- vertex (vertices)

One way to describe a geometric solid is to identify the number of faces, edges, and vertices it has.

A face is a 2-D figure that makes up a flat surface of a 3-D solid.	An edge is the line segment where two faces meet.	A vertex is the point at the corner where edges meet.

A rectangular prism has the following features:

6 faces	12 edges	8 vertices
(You can not see all of the faces in this picture.)		

How many faces does this triangular prism have?
What do the faces look like?
How many edges does it have?
How many vertices does it have?

one hundred twenty-one SMH 121

Math Words and Ideas, p. 121

Math Words and Ideas

Solids and Silhouettes

(page 1 of 2)

Math Words
- silhouette

A silhouette is a flat, dark shape produced when an object blocks light. It is like a shadow. The light from this lamp is creating a silhouette of this girl's face. In the silhouette you can see the outline of her profile, but not the features of her face.

Andrew's class is examining the silhouettes made by different geometric solids.

Andrew: *The square prism can make a tall, skinny rectangular silhouette or a square silhouette, depending on its position and how the light hits it.*

SMH 122 one hundred twenty-two

Math Words and Ideas, p. 122

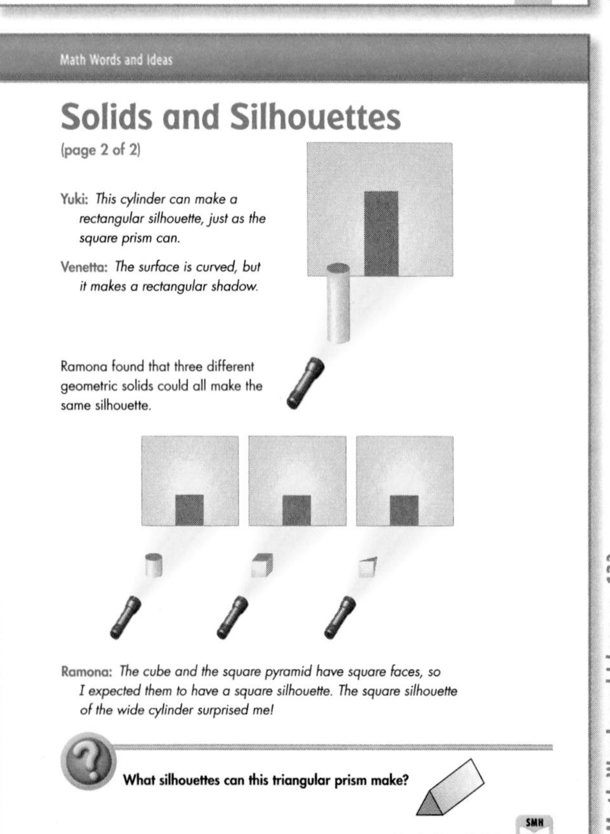

Math Words and Ideas

Solids and Silhouettes

(page 2 of 2)

Yuki: *This cylinder can make a rectangular silhouette, just as the square prism can.*

Venetta: *The surface is curved, but it makes a rectangular shadow.*

Ramona found that three different geometric solids could all make the same silhouette.

Ramona: *The cube and the square pyramid have square faces, so I expected them to have a square silhouette. The square silhouette of the wide cylinder surprised me!*

What silhouettes can this triangular prism make?

one hundred twenty-three SMH 123

Math Words and Ideas, p. 123

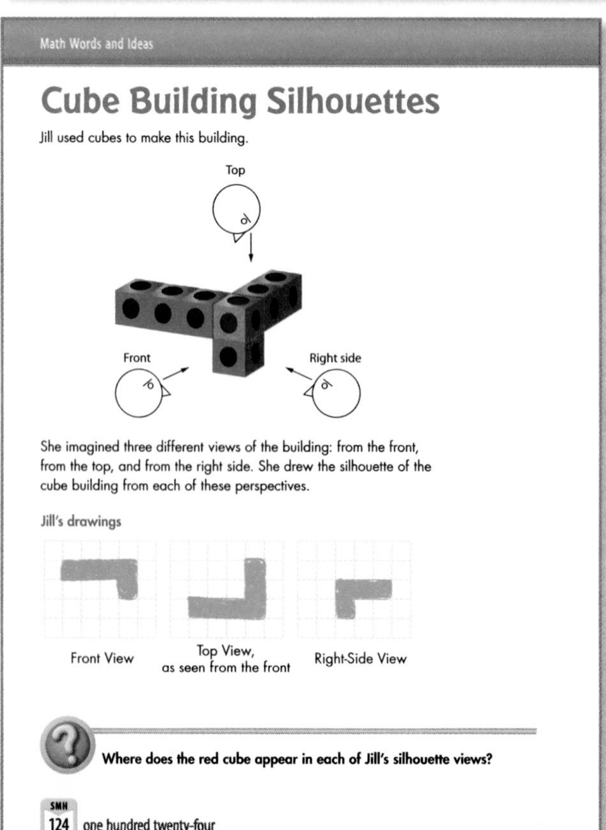

Math Words and Ideas

Cube Building Silhouettes

Jill used cubes to make this building.

She imagined three different views of the building: from the front, from the top, and from the right side. She drew the silhouette of the cube building from each of these perspectives.

Jill's drawings

Where does the red cube appear in each of Jill's silhouette views?

SMH 124 one hundred twenty-four

Math Words and Ideas, p. 124

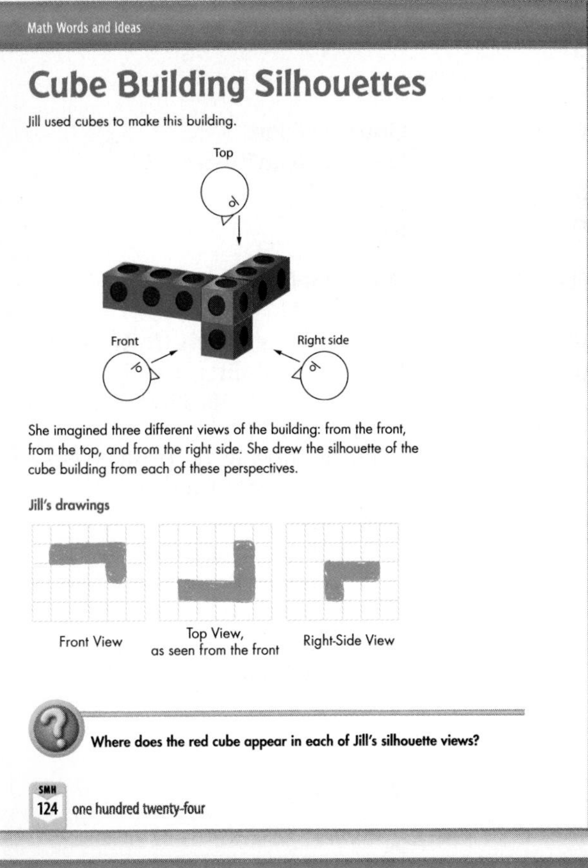

Math Words and Ideas

Cube Building Silhouettes

Jill used cubes to make this building.

She imagined three different views of the building: from the front, from the top, and from the right side. She drew the silhouette of the cube building from each of these perspectives.

Jill's drawings

Where does the red cube appear in each of Jill's silhouette views?

SMH 124 one hundred twenty-four

Math Words and Ideas, p. 124

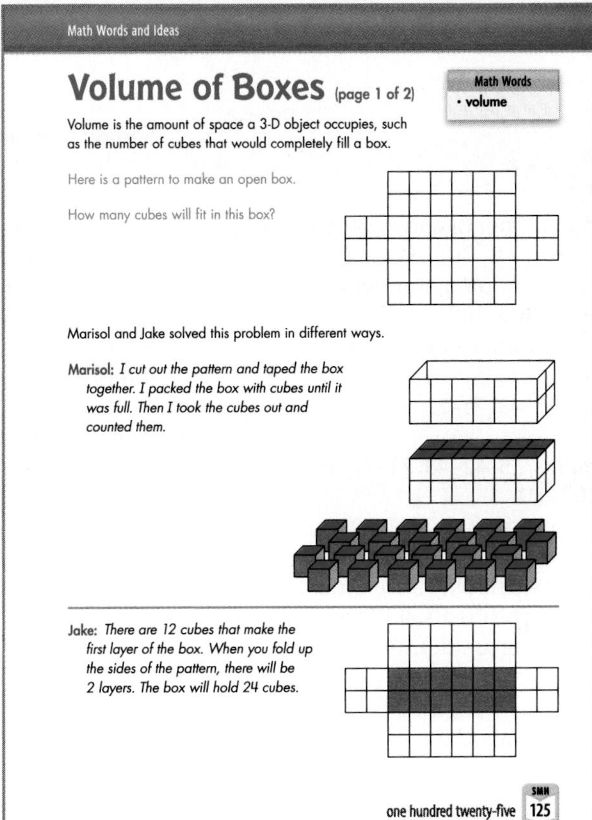

Math Words and Ideas

Volume of Boxes (page 1 of 2)

Math Words
- volume

Volume is the amount of space a 3-D object occupies, such as the number of cubes that would completely fill a box.

Here is a pattern to make an open box.

How many cubes will fit in this box?

Marisol and Jake solved this problem in different ways.

Marisol: *I cut out the pattern and taped the box together. I packed the box with cubes until it was full. Then I took the cubes out and counted them.*

Jake: *There are 12 cubes that make the first layer of the box. When you fold up the sides of the pattern, there will be 2 layers. The box will hold 24 cubes.*

one hundred twenty-five SMH 125

Math Words and Ideas, p. 125

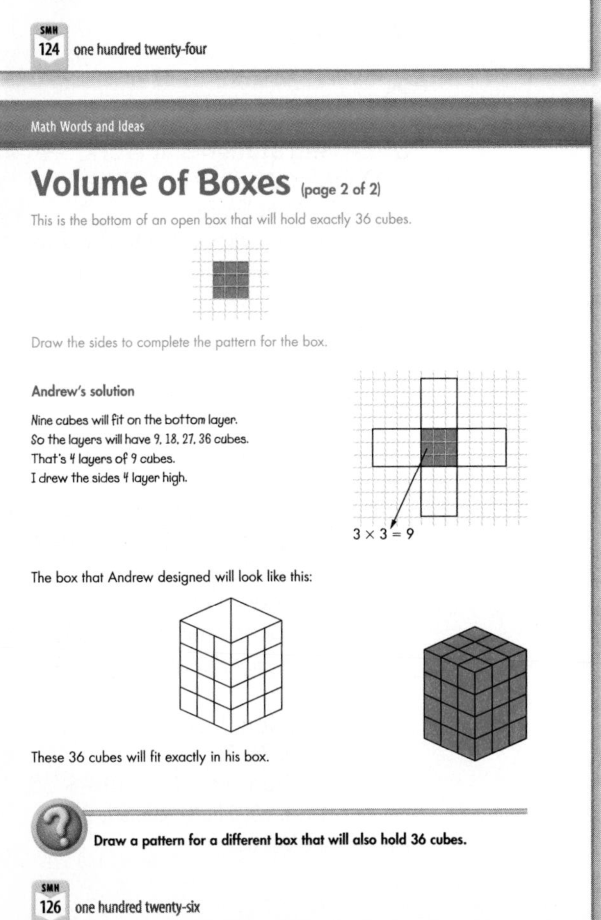

Math Words and Ideas

Volume of Boxes (page 2 of 2)

This is the bottom of an open box that will hold exactly 36 cubes.

Draw the sides to complete the pattern for the box.

Andrew's solution

Nine cubes will fit on the bottom layer.
So the layers will have 9, 18, 27, 36 cubes.
That's 4 layers of 9 cubes.
I drew the sides 4 layer high.

The box that Andrew designed will look like this:

These 36 cubes will fit exactly in his box.

Draw a pattern for a different box that will also hold 36 cubes.

SMH 126 one hundred twenty-six

Math Words and Ideas, p. 126

Index

IN THIS UNIT

W